I Want To Really Learn About Horses

T.J. Gillespie

First Published in 2010 by TAF Publishing.

This edition published by The Manuscript Publisher, 2018.

ISBN: 978-1-911442-12-7
A CIP Catalogue record for this book is available from the National Library

Typesetting and Cover Design by
DocumentsandManuscripts.com

Gaelic Ruler Setting Out on a Journey on Horseback
used courtesy of the National Library of Ireland

I Want To Really Learn About Horses

Acknowledgments

I wish to express my gratitude to Noel French the Director and the staff and trainees of Trim Forum for Employment for their assistance with typing, compilation and transmission of contents of this book.

Also to Messrs. Oscar Duggan and David Jones of The Authors Friend and management/staff of Gemini Press.

It is well-nigh impossible to quantify the information/wisdom gleaned from people like William Flood, Boardsmill Stud, the Veterinary practices of Clarke and Gibbons; Pat Farrelly; Desmond Kavanagh/Raphael Warner and from farriers Messrs Harnan, Keane and Madden.

Scores of others who may now have 'left the stage' sowed the seed for this book – they are still in my mind's 'eye'.

I was/still am a devotee of veterinary articles in The Irish Field, Horse and Hound and other periodicals, likewise articles and publications relating to horse care and equitation.

How I interpreted/used this information is of course my responsibility.

I would always advocate good safe practice knowing it builds confidence and competence and wish every reader happiness and enjoyment with their horse/pony.

T.J. Gillespie

Front cover: 'Briany Boru', gelding by Clover Hill x Westfield Diamond, owned by the author, bred in Co. Limerick, exported to Edmonton, Canada.
Back Cover: 'Hugh de Lacy' grazing at Yellow Steeple; Author 'resting.'

The Good Shepherd

The Good Shepherd

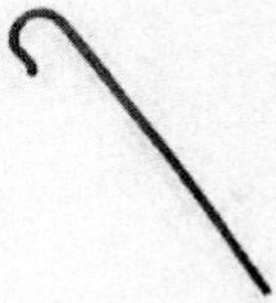

Every winter's night a solitary figure steps out the road from Thomastown.

Here's how you'll know him;

'Tidy bundle of hay under one arm; quarter-filled meal bag in the other'!

"I'll stop for a chat"

Wintry squalls tormented us but Pat was not bothered.

"Clover Hill; Ballinvella; Smooth Stepper; Delmaine; a great horsewoman from Kinnity and someone from Clondra."

I took my leave "stock of my own" and 'tipped' back to Trim.

Strange how the parable of the Good Shepherd kept coming to mind.

When next I heard, Pat was dead and buried.

They say Peter himself was 'on the gate'.

"Come in a mhic-Come in"!

Down here we just say "may the green sod rest lightly on your grave, Pat."

T.J.G.

Appreciation of Pat Coffey, Thomastown, Killucan, died 8th May 1995.

Contents

Part One: One thing missed by not knowing
Nine by not looking

1. Safety	1-3
2. Common Ailments	
- Lameness	4-10
- Coughing, Chills, Flu	11
3. Drugs	12
4. Parasites	13-16
5. Colic	17-18
6. Lungs	19-20
7. Heart and Circulatory System	21-22
8. A Few More Things	23-28
9. Matchstick Horse at Rest	31-32
10. Foaling, Weaning, Sales Preparation	35-39

Part Two: Follow Your Dream

11. Getting Started	42-46
12. Suppling Exercises	47-49
13. Gaits of the Horse Theory and Practice	50-55
14. More Mental Blocks	56-57
15. Another First-outing (Travelling by box)	58
16. Clipping	59-60
17. The Awkward Cuss	61-62
18. 'Prepping' a Horse for Racing	63-65
19. Marking Chart and Colours of Horses	69
20. A Bit of History	70-71
Index	73

Part One
1. Safety-Working with Animals

'Disease's/infections' possible!

Tetanus:	Bacterial disease: associated with horses' bedding; dung-heaps -can survive anaerobically/without oxygen. Can enter through puncture wounds; very serious. Programmed vaccination essential.
Leptospirosis (Weil's disease):	Associated mainly with rats/rat-runs; infection distributed in rat urine. Protective gloves where contamination likely. Med. Advice re. any inoculation.
Brucellosis:	Not as widespread as formerly; due to eradication programme in cows. Illness in humans; fever-like; recurring over years. Care still handling 'after birth'(placenta) of cows/ mares particularly applies to women/girls.
Rabies:	Very strict control at borders/country boundaries has curtailed spread. A neurological infection in dogs/foxes/wolves/cats and bats. Symptoms 'dog' foaming at the mouth; violent (rabid); Infection well-nigh fatal to humans; Inoculation/vaccine.
Ringworm:	Disease of fungal nature-highly contagious-spread by calves ➔ horse's ➔ humans; painful; irritating. Horses may be inspected at racecourses, shows, sales rings, for signs of ringworm and if positive will not be allowed entry to prevent spread of disease. Medicinal food additives for number of days will clear up trouble in horses but 'spores' of 'fungus'

may still cling to tack; stable furnishings; gate posts.
Sunlight will kill those spores.

Farmers Lung Disease: Caused by inhaling spores in 'mouldy' hay.
Precautions; wear mask.
Not so prevalent now as haylage and silage have replaced a big portion of hay-making.

Working with Horses-Safety

Advisable to wear strong (steel-capped) boots; horse treading on foot/toes can inflict serious injury.
Use proper lead-ropes-Not nylon 'baler twine'; can 'burn' skin.
Do not wrap lead ropes around hand-entanglement-serious injury!
If 'tying-up' horse use 'slip-knot'; best if swivel in catch!

Horse with 'kicking' propensity; it'll be the hind ones': perhaps nervous/defence reaction or plain malice.
With any strange horse stand close, 'place hand firmly on neck to inspire confidence and
'advance'-shoulder ➔ back ➔ loins ➔ rump ➔ down flank ➔ hock all the time uttering reassuring not nervous notes and presenting angular aspect of body; vital areas not exposed!

You want to 'pick out' hoof;
Let him know, "Hugo give me this piggy".
Grasp at fetlock joint, squeeze with fingers to reinforce message.
He'll 'lift' eventually; maybe try to pull it away; 'hang on; go with it'; utter appropriate imprecations.
Usually he'll soon accept the inevitable unless he's really wild or a right 'wrong one':
So you've won 'round one.'
He's got a good introduction; he'll be O.K. for rest of his life

Note: 'restraints' can be used 'in difficult cases'!
Twitch ('touch') applied to upper lip or by hand grasping 'fold of skin' on neck.

Foals: leading/handling foals' demands awareness and understanding.
Teaching foal to lead; first steps, 'gentle' him/her alongside 'mammy'; reassures both; do not 'drag' or 'push'; instinctive reaction is to 'rear up'; or ' kick out'
Young body is so flexible handler can suffer very serious injury:
Minimize presentation of head, face, body area in 'danger-zone'!
With tact/patience will come success, but handler should remain vigilant particularly in new situations e.g. show classes.

2. Common Ailments of Horses

Lameness:

Lameness indicates horse/pony is in pain and trying to mitigate pain by altering 'gait'. Degree of lameness may be: -

a. Mild; barely perceptible,
b. Obviously lame,
c. 'On three legs'

In all cases he/she must be 'rested;' further exercise may worsen injury; prompt attention is essential.

To ascertain 'in which leg,' 'Trot horse up'.

Horse will 'favour' lame leg i.e. try to keep weight off it;

a. By lifting head/neck if it's a fore leg.
b. Quarters on lame side will be higher if it's a hind leg.

Visual Examination. Any obvious wound? inflammation/heat?

If nothing strikingly obvious; Rule is-'Horse is lame in hoof till proved otherwise'.

Stone Bruise is the most common type of hoof injury: 'as easy to get as wet feet'.

Horse treads on stone/sharp object, bruising of blood-rich tissue within 'solid box' of hoof; turns septic; becomes progressively more painful.

Farrier will locate tender area in sole and makes neat incision to allow pus to escape.

Poultice applied for say three days; then 'dry-up' and horse re-shod.

Keep on 'good ground' for some time to allow to heal fully (See diagram below).

Note:

- Poulticing was/is widely used in bringing an abscess/hidden infection to a head; aids in 'draining' and with hygienic practice leads to rapid healing. Formerly a very effective poultice for hoof wounds was Epsom salts dissolved in glycerine and applied liberally to hoof with protective covering enclosing hoof.

Ready made poulticing/dressing products are now widely available.

- Periodic walking of paddocks/exercise arenas-picking stones; looking for broken rails/loose wire/glass and other hazards is essential.

'If an accident can happen-it will happen.'

Hoof

Coronary Band.
Hoof grows down from Coronary Band-can stimulate growth by rubbing a mild 'blister' into Coronary band.

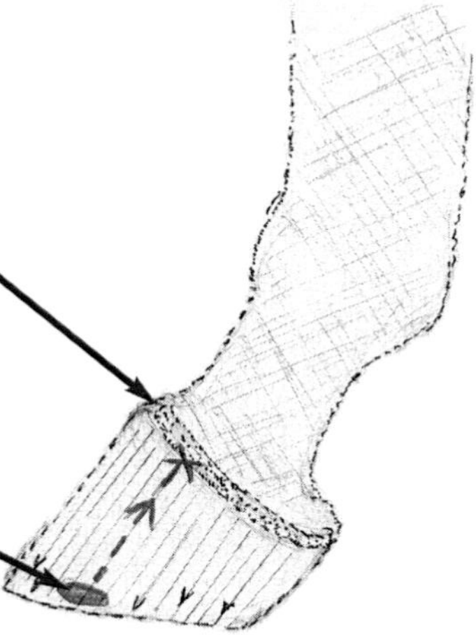

Result of stone bruise; sepsis will travel upwards.
If neglected abscess will emerge at coronary band, and 'weakness' at this point in hoof wall will take at least 6 months to grow down to sole.

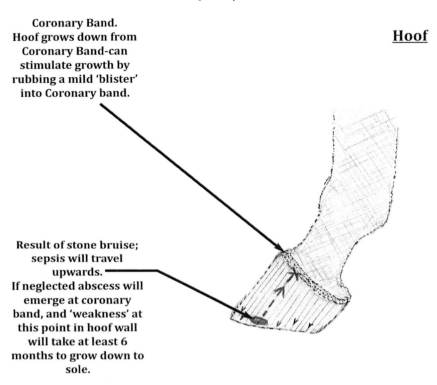

Hoof Underneath

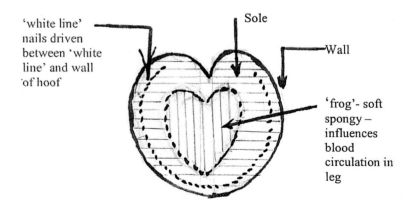

'white line' nails driven between 'white line' and wall of hoof

Sole

Wall

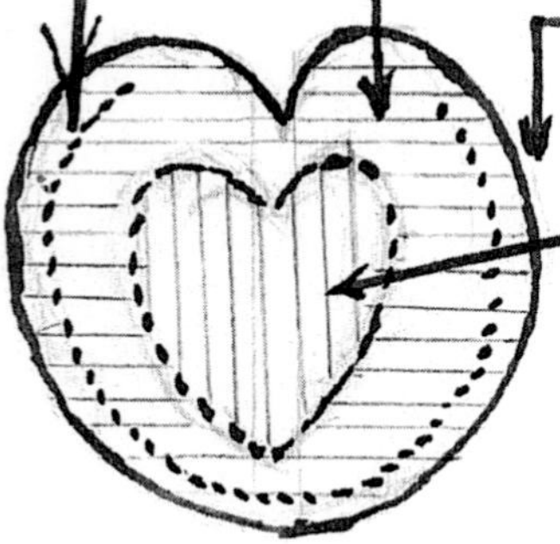

'frog'- soft spongy – influences blood circulation in leg

Cuts and abrasions are a common form of injury

Visual Examination:

- Is it recent-still bleeding?
- Is it surface only or deeper?
- On or near joint?
- Can horse walk or too painful?
- Is stitching required:, has he got his anti-tet.?

(At this stage experienced person will decide if vet, should be called.)

If 'you' feel competent to treat injury:

Bring horse into stable or restricted area.

Procure First Aid Kit, and clip hair round wound with blunt-nosed scissors; allows to drain better.

Irrigate with mild saline solution. No Hosing; jet of water would wash out healing serum/ colourless fluid.

Remove any 'foreign bodies,' grass/twigs/ clay, with tweezers.

Do not use iodine or sprays-too caustic.

If wound is deep, moderate splash of hydrogen peroxide 'fizzes up' and can carry contaminants to the surface.

Pat gently with sterile tissue.

Apply non-stick dressing and bandage just sufficiently to keep in place; excludes dirt and by allowing air to circulate promotes healing.

Later, if dressing stays on don't interfere-unless there are signs of infection; heat, inflammation, blood or pus seeping out.

If so, do not neglect; inspect and take appropriate action.

If wound heals 'over' some 'foreign body' e.g. pebble, fragment of bone; the site will suppurate at regular intervals (Horse goes out to grass; height of growing season, June/July, white blood cells are 'stoked-up,' 'go to war' on dormant infection).

Lameness, Injury of Competition Horses

Injuries to ligaments, tendons, joints and bone are incurred by competition horses.

Skilful treatment and 'time'/rest is essential for proper recovery.

Understanding the 'nature' of these vulnerable 'parts' will help to avoid/minimize costly 'down time.'

Cartilage, ligaments, tendons, bone are rich in collagen, a gelatinous substance of 'living' protein, B complex amino acids, arranged in fibres.

Programmed exercise called conditioning; making 'fit'; 'strengthens' cartilage, ligaments, tendons and bone by a process thought to be 'bunching up'; making fibre 'bundles' more 'dense'.

These components are then better able to accommodate the stresses and strains of competition.

Basically their functions are:

I. Cartilage, cushioning and 'lubricating' within joints.

II. Ligaments, 'binding' around joint to keep in place.

III. Tendons are totally inelastic fibrous cords: transferring 'pull' from muscles to articulate joints.

IV. Bone; skeleton; 'frame work'; 'chassis,' covers ground, of mainly calcium composition.

Tearing of a ligament is usually caused by twisting or awkward movement; particularly the suspensory ligament in front legs.

Will be indicated by 'heat', inflammation, puffiness of tissue.

Rest in stable; further exercise will worsen the condition.

Cool with trickle of water from hose pipe or apply crushed-ice pack.

Cooling contracts tissue, forces blood and oedema away from site.

After cooling apply compression/support bandage firmly but not restricting circulation.

a. Bandage both legs as horse may lean all weight on 'good' leg!

b. Apply 'dab' of unpleasant unguent to bandages to deter mischief; feed horse hay, bran mash; no oats/heating food.

Don't rush: recovery takes at least a week to ten days (by comparison with muscles, blood supply to ligaments and tendons is poor).

First day out, with quiet companion, leave bandages on in case of 'mad' galloping.

Tendons move in lubricated (synovial fluid) sheaths for protection.

In young animals the tendon is crimped; severe usage causes 'elongation' and may lead to 'breaking-down' associated with fatigue towards end of race/event; recovery is slow.

Another less serious form of injury is 'rapped' tendon; a blow perhaps from opposite leg 'bruises' tendon sheath; inflammation; fluid/blood in sheath.

Administer drug to reduce inflammation/disperse fluid or can lance sheath and drain spurious fluid.

In either case take care that 'adhesions' don't arise; sheath might heal to tendon!

Note: Walking horses on hard even surfaces e.g. 'road work,' strengthens tendons and ligaments; has definite role in promoting competitive fitness.

IV. Bone

Most problems, associated with bone in the horse's legs only become apparent when 'his' training commences

- Splints,

In the Mesozoic era between 65 and 24 million years ago the horse was three toed and about the height of a fox.

In the intervening years the two side toes 'regressed; now they are independent bones on either side of main cannon bone.

When young horse is put into work they may 'fuse' (tissue ossifies to 'bone') to the cannon bone; with inflammation, 'heat,' pain while happening.

With strengthening of bone; perhaps ease in work and cooling embrocation the condition may subside; horses may 'grow out' of splints.

Some horses may be genetically disposed; their bone may be 'soft,' diet calcium deficient?

- 'Sore Shins'

May afflict young horses when first being trained for racing-also occur in human athletes particularly long distance runners.

Caused by inflammation of the periosteum; shiny membrane coating front of shin/cannon bone.

It tends to tear away from bone, disturbing nerve-endings, causing pain. Treatment, again cooling, anti-inflammatory drugs, exercise on soft surface.

Author's opinion: If horse is set to do 'fast work' /exercise wrap front legs above fetlock joint to under knee with 'generous' cotton wool layer & bandage securely; 'disaster' if bandage unwinds during galloping.

Leave bandage on after exercise or remove, hose with cold water, pat dry, replace bandage.

Above applies particularly to young horses on firm summer ground; time/effort worthwhile as 'sore shins' will interrupt training programme.'

- Ring Bones/Side Bones; describe a condition sometime seen in young half- bred horses.

A hard 'tissue to bony' growth in pastern area; with anti-inflammatory drugs and less intense 'work' condition may stabilize.

Note:

a. It is known that bone is strengthened by correct form of force e.g. the young horse's bones (legs in particular and front legs more so) are strengthened by hitting the ground; galloping; but achieving 'happy medium' is the art; too much and risk splints; sore shins!

b. Relating mainly to high profile thoroughbred racehorses, occurrence of 'stress fractures,' split pasterns and similar are occasionally reported.
Bone is involved in each case; skilled surgery/remedial work can/may restore horse to competitive level or useful retirement.

Two very serious conditions whose onset is gradual/insidious are:

I. Laminitis (coming from Latin laminae-leaves) is a crippling condition arising in the hoof.

The blood-rich tissue within the hoof is affixed to the 'external' wall by an array of laminae.

Any inflammation there is called laminitis; more prevalent in ponies (native of a sparse environment) who are allowed to graze luxuriant pastures, mid-summer, and not given the work/exercise load to match.

The conformation/location of bones within hoof becomes distorted and very painful. Drug treatment/remedial farriery may improve situation.

If ground is hard old remedy was stand/exercise in 'pudding' of clay & water.

Distortion within hoof may be irreversible and ponies' useful career jeopardized!

Laminitis may appear in mares if portion of after birth (placenta) is retained-septicaemia sets in; very, very serious.

II. Navicular

This very painful condition is a wastage/deterioration of a small pivotal bone in the hoof: healthy bone/tissue is nourished by an adequate blood supply-the navicular bone has perforations to facilitate blood flow.

The horse is a creature of movement-there are no valves in 'his' leg veins; blood circulation is promoted by compression/expansion of 'frog in hoof through exercise.

Big, strong, half-bred horses of middle age, 7-12 yrs, e.g. hunters are most at risk.

Prevention: turn out in paddock on 'off' days.

When condition is noticed vet. consulted who may prescribe an anti-coagulant drug.

This enhances blood flow and may restore bone:

Other recommendations: inject cortisone through top of heel. Also remedial farriery, rounding/shortening 'toe' reduces 'leverage' on navicular bone; working life of horse may be extended.

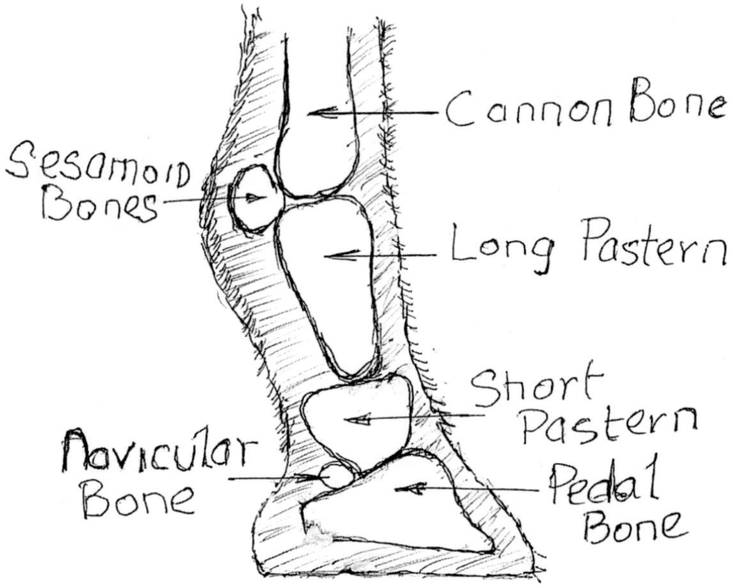

Coughing, Chills, Flu..

If a horse is heard to cough investigate immediately.

(a) Is horse off feed? If stabled: check feeding-pot.
If at grass is he grazing in company or standing isolated; hunched-up?

(b) Runny-nose?

(c) Check temp. by inserting mercury bulb of standard 'stick' thermometer in anus; leave for a few minutes. Normal 100.5/101°F 37.5/38°C; Raised 103/104/105°F/40°C.
While temp. is raised definitely No Exercise,

(d) Has horse had anti-flu. vac?

(e) Isolate from other horse to prevent infection spreading.
Good air circulation in stable but no draughts: ideally stables have chicken mesh to ceiling-sparrows can carry infection!

(f) Light-warm rug; clean fresh water available, tempt with small freshly-made bran mash, chopped carrots, apples.

Clean tub, small wad of hay, tablespoon of treacle, scald with kettle of boiling water, palatable: steam assists in clearing mucous.

Contact Vet:, "any other outbreaks in Area?"

He will probably advise; "Monitor; if no improvement in 24hrs, let me know".

(g) When infection clears up, temp. back to normal, appetite returns, horse may still cough, throat sensitive, perhaps difficulty swallowing dry food: -

(i) Try dab of honey to back of tongue.

(ii) Mustard poultice to throat; steam/eucalyptus inhalant.

(iii) lead out for 'pick' of grass-lowering of head assists in clearing sinus cavities, and assists air intake, straighter 'run' through trachea (windpipe).

Note: Coughs, chills flu may 'pass' in adult horses. Virus Pneumonia is a 'killer' in foals, often within 24 hours.

3. Drugs, When and How to Administer

To anyone caring for horses the terms non-steroidal, anti-inflammatory drugs (NSAID's) are 'as common as snuff at a wake.'

These NSAID's have analgesic (pain killing) properties also, so horse can recover, from injury/surgery in comfort.

Vet. will advise re. dosage and any possible side effects e.g. danger to in-foal mare.

Note:

- Misuse arises if a drug is administered to 'mask' lameness.
- Appropriate regulating authorities stipulate certain 'threshold' levels (in the blood) 'or zero tolerance' for certain drugs termed 'performance enhancing'/ 'prohibited' substances'
- For a 16.2h.h. 500kg 'patient' a vet. may prescribe: "Add two 5grm sachets (contains 1grm 'bute') of 'bute' to 'his' feed, morning and evening, for two days and 1 sachet twice a day for next four days and I will review then".
- To exceed dosage or administer without advice is dangerous.

Penicillin/Streptomycin are antibiotic substances effective against disease bacteria.

A healthy horse will have an immune system able to withstand infection.

Antibiotics only called upon when immune system fails.

Unwise to employ antibiotics as 'matter of course'; they have inhibiting effect on 'useful' bacteria in horse gut/digestive system – (pro-biotics-supplemental feed to maximize efficiency of gut).

Modes of Injection:

1.Subcutaneous/under the skin.

2.Intramuscular/into muscle; sometimes there is a reaction; inflammation arises; so pick muscle in chest (not too obvious);or in rump; (horse may resent; danger of kicking; hold up fore leg.)

3.Intravenous (into vein; main blood stream) is effective; quick acting/antibiotic is diluted/carried in blood flow.

Care/skill required to guard against air/oxygen entering blood stream.

4. Parasites

Parasites: seriously affect the health/performance/comfort of animals.
Internally: as ascarids, strongyles migrating through alimentary system; bloodstream and liver.
Externally: as lice, fleas.

Internal parasites are controlled by regular dosing with anthelmintic drugs (wormers) taking account of seasonal variations, age of animals and possible build- up of 'resistance' to the drug.
Worm doses are given on an empty stomach as programmed/for horses going out to grass or coming in from grass to start training programme.
An animal with heavy "worm" infestation will look 'poor', dry of coat.
To get definite 'picture' a worm egg-count in droppings can be done.

Worm dosing in Practice (primarily to horse/ponies)

Rule 1. On Empty stomach

(a) Ingredients can be mixed with lukewarm water in a bucket and administered by stomach tube to patient(s). Requires skill/practice, not widely used now; if large numbers possibly!
(b) By granules in feed.
The horse's palate is sensitive to 'strange' tastes. Use 'mind games'.
(i)Sachets stored in fridge; taste/scent not as dominant.
(ii)Total dose in portion of feed then 'top up' with remainder of feed to 'mop up' particles 'pushed to side of plate'
(c) More commonly by 'syringe paste'.
Ensure no 'gob' of food in mouth.
Discharge syringe on back of tongue, holding tongue perhaps to keep mouth open. Hold up head; tickle throat to induce to swallow (some 'born actors' will grimace fearfully to indicate displeasure).
'Drenching gun' widely used for cattle; require safe 'crush'; still strenuous, hazardous work.
Latterly 'pour on' based on ivermectin applied to dry spinal ridge, 'filtering' through skin; is widely advertised for cattle.
Not used on horses, though an oral wormer based on ivermectin is popular

Note: - Prudent to study 'literature' from each manufacturer.
i. Dosing interval
ii. What it 'kills'
iii. Build up of resistance
iv. Any 'special offers'!!

N.B. Fluke normally associated with cattle/sheep; wet /damp conditions favour, very debilitating: (treat with 'pour on') (fluke not unknown in foals-horse's).

Equipment-Worm egg Count Test.

I. Microscope low powered lens i.e. x 8 eyepiece x objective lens
II. Slide
III. Fine mesh strainer.

Sample of faeces (size of walnut), (2grms-if very accurate count required).
Saturated saline solution-no more salt will dissolve.
Empty container; faecal sample, adequate saline solution.
Mix very well, filter liquid through mesh, squeeze all liquid out.
Fill both chambers of slide; allow to settle, eggs will float to surface.
Place slide on microscope and focus, so width between a pair of tram-lines can be seen.
Count no, of individual types of eggs.
Count both chambers, total number of eggs of each variety found x 50 gives no. of eggs per gram of faeces.

Worm Eggs Under The Microscope

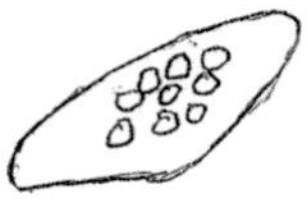

Strongyle (Red Worm) (Blood Suckers) By far most important Migrate through intestinal walls Damage gut- intermittent colic

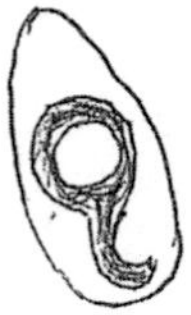

Stronyloide

Ascarid (Round Worm) (Young Horse)

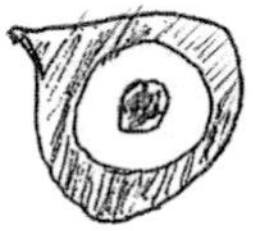

Tape Worm

The donkey is host to lung worm, seldom cause much harm to him; if transferred to horse may produce symptoms of coughing and broken wind.

Worm Egg Count acceptable level up to 200 eggs/grm.; Dosing required above 200 eggs/grm., 1000 eggs/grm of sample, SERIOUS.

To prevent paddocks continually grazed by horse's becoming 'sour' and source of worm infestation.

(i) Horse 'Droppings' should ideally be gathered every day using wheelbarrow and shovel!

Chain-harrowing; spreading/dispersing is only 'half measure' at best

(ii) Lime dressing applied before growing season.

(iii) Interval or rotational grazing e.g. horses followed by bullocks; grazing patterns and parasite species differ from equine to bovine.

Horse uses incisors; 'loves' grass 5 cms. to 7.5cms. in height.

Bullock wraps 'rough' tongue round 'tussock' & 'tugs' it up

Grazing pattern of horse & sheep are similar; both use incisors to 'cut' early growth/fresh 'shoots'

Lactating animals-Mare, Cow, ewe will 'extract' calcium and proteins from pasture; 'growing' animals; calves, foals, lambs will do likewise.

Note: Digestive system of horses, inefficient by comparison with bovines.
Calorific extractions, Horse order of 50%, bovine over 90%.

External Parasites:

Lice can be serious bloodsucking parasites.
They live comfortably in hair; skin scurf of horses/cattle.
In case of horses it is most effective to clip out body hair completely (burn or dispose otherwise of hair), shampoo thoroughly and rug up when dry.
Lice and other harmful agents e.g. streptococcus equine; ring worm; eye-infections, can survive in nooks/crannies of old stables.
So routine steam cleaning or lime washing of walls is good policy.
With cattle dusting with delousing powder may be used; not recommended for horses.

5. Colic

(An archaic name for pain in the stomach)

The horse's digestive system is 'programmed' to 'little and often'.
In nature he 'nibbles a bit,' moves on, 'nibbles' again.
His system can be upset by irregular feeding times, abrupt change in diet (grazing to dry feeding or vice versa), change in environment, stress/fatigue; contaminated food.

The upset can develop; stoppage, fermentation of food material, gas, pain.
Symptoms: uneasy, sweating, rolling, kicking out.

First Aid: Walking may 'trigger' movement of bowels and experienced person may endeavour to clear blockage using arm-length polythene glove lubricated with liquid of paraffin.
Vet. on arrival will most likely adopt same course having given relaxing drug to horse.
Note: In addition to indigestible food, cysts/ lesions on lining of gut, caused by worms, can contribute to blockages.

Colic Prevention

i. Regular feeding: demulcent added to feed (assists in swallowing).
ii. Attention to teeth; adequate chewing of food.

Horse 'chewing' is a sideways movement of jaws, a grinding action;
Outer edges of upper teeth/inner edges of lower teeth may develop 'hooks' causing discomfort to tongue and lining of mouth.
Corrected by 'floating'/rasping.
iii. Add bulk (e.g. chaff: chopped up carrots) to feed to prevent 'bolting' of food.
iv. On No Account let horse near lawnmower cuttings or let out stabled horse into freshly 'topped' paddock.
v. Twisted gut may follow from colic and 'odds on' require surgery.

Formerly the horse was regarded as 'poor' subject for surgery.

Latterly it is realized that loss of body fluid up to 10 litres-12 litres and resulting shock was a contributory factor to the high mortality rate.

Use of intravenous drip improves prognosis.

Note: 'Round Feeders' dispose towards gluttony!

'Junior is determined to eat as much as his bigger 'neighbour'; see the signs;- distended abdomen.

6. Lungs

Imagine two flexible airtight sacks 'lined' with numerous tiny sacs (aveoli) which are laced with capillaries; fine-bore blood vessels.

By 'osmosis' oxygen from air intake passes into the red corpuscles of the blood stream.

At rest respiration, in/out, is 8 -12 per minute.

The horse by reason of his high speed locomotion (maximum recorded on turf 42 m.p.h) is a "drinker of the wind," Arab expression.

Air volume breathed at rest approximately 80 litres/min; during severe exercise it may reach 800 litres/min.

Under severe exercise (flat out gallop) respirations may be in range 120 to 200/min.

Note also extension of nostrils, with incorporated blood vessels to 'warm up' incoming air.

Healthy lungs are vital to a horse!

The sacs can be damaged/ruptured irreparably by infection; dust; spores/mildew (hay/straw); pneumonia; exercise when unfit/running a temperature.

'Broken Wind' (Emphysema) may result; will be detected and noted by vet.

Horse 'breathes in' during suspension phase of canter/gallop (all legs off ground).

Vet. testing horse's 'wind,' 'does he make a noise'? will want horse galloped or lunged.

Note:

1. Some racehorses subject to 'wind trouble' are best trained 'off the field'; fresh air rather than stable atmosphere suiting them better; avoiding lush pasture of course!
2. A herd of cattle will 'cough' after a jog of less than 100m; illustrating different roles.

Strangles

Strangles is a streptococcal highly contagious disease of the lymph glands around the throat.

Young growing horses, perhaps ill-nourished, or stressed due to travelling, appear most susceptible.

Normal Course: abscess developing; inflammation; temperature up to 40°C, difficulty in swallowing.

Abscess bursts, discharges; assist drainage, bathe, isolate animal, dispose of dressings with care. With attention wound will heal in a few days; animal will now have immunity but requires 'building up'.

In the more serious case the abscess develops and bursts internally; infection can now descend into lungs; requiring intensive antibiotic treatment if 'wind' is not to be 'touched' i.e. lungs damaged.

Infection can persist in stables; steam cleaning advisable.

Highly irresponsible to knowingly allow other horses to share stable yard/surroundings with affected or recovering horse!

7. Heart and Circulatory System:

The heart pumps blood through the circulatory system starting at main output artery, the aorta, and extending to a network of fine capillaries.

It is a muscular unit comprising various cavities, chambers and valves whose healthy condition is essential to efficient functioning.

Their well - being, like that of other muscles, is impaired by infection 'agents' invading the blood stream; confirming the necessity of clamping down on 'trouble making' intestinal worms and avoiding 'unclean things' like 'strangles' (streptococcus equi).
Listening with stethoscope to the heart 'is an education'.
The trained person can 'interpret' its performance; are there any anomalies? missed beats; murmurs?
An electrocardiograph (ECG) will give the 'picture' in 'black and white'.
To the lay person the 'thumping' of a foal's heart; or any young animal's is 'music,' sound so distinct; suffers no attenuation through layers of fat and muscle.
The heart beat/pulse at rest 36 -42 beats per minute; in young horse slightly higher; very fit horse slightly less.
At high level exercise e.g. flat-out gallop, pulse rate can rise to 250 per minute.

Healthy lungs supply oxygen to red corpuscles in blood stream that 'transport' it 'down the line' to muscles 'great and small'.
Exercise - 'work' enlarges muscles; carbohydrates burn efficiently with oxygen/aerobically..
If insufficient oxygen lactic acid, a toxin, is generated and fatigue results.
Fit, well conditioned, muscles are thought to store oxygen.
So rule is: To carry out serious exercise an athlete must be conditioned, made 'fit' through ascending exercise loads to service/accomplish 'new peaks'.

Notes

1. It takes seven days/ stages to reach summit of Mt. Kilimanjaro, ht. 5.9 km.

On the middle four days there's 'funny carry-on'.
You do your appointed trek; go on another few hundred metres 'for practice' then drop back to the camp for the night.
It's called 'acclimatization,' air is getting thinner; lungs must 'think a bit bigger'.
By morning day 7 you're 'sucking diesel,' 'acclimatized;' fit for final lunge!

2. Heart muscle enlarged; 'sign of superior athlete'!
3. Heart of great racehorse Eclipse (foaled 1764-year of eclipse) weighed 14 lbs at autopsy.
   Eclipse never beaten: flat races were run in 'heats' then; distances of three to four miles were common.
4. The horse's pulse rate can be felt/measured where a vein comes against/crosses a bone; a convenient place is about midway along underside of lower jaw.

8. A Few More 'Things'

a. Wolf Tooth/Teeth

A vestige of canine tooth may be found in both jaws in front of molars– about size of very small orange pip; not in fillies/mares; has no roots; may interfere with bit; better extracted; a simple procedure.

b. Sweet Itch

An allergy to the saliva of a biting midge; condition seems virtually unknown outside of some 'native' ponies and part 'cold-blood' horses.

Affected horse/pony will scratch the irritating area; usually head; crest of neck/mane; rump/tail/dock, 'breaking' hair and skin.

Application of creams; benzyl benzoate/camomile lotion will ease discomfort. Various homeopathic remedies are promoted.

In practice wearing a light, generous fitting screening rug/sheet covering head, neck, body and extending well over rump/dock 'frustrates' midge who is most active in mornings /evenings.

c. Photo-Sensitivity

Not common; caused by horse eating plant St. John's Wort causing liver reaction which makes white haired areas sensitive to sunlight; skin cracks and weeps. Treatment: Mitigate exposure to sunlight at critical time: keep indoors or try designing 'sun-screen' bandage

d. Pollen Allergies

The quantity/variety of pollen circulating in an 'old meadow' as distinct from rigorously managed paddock is considerable.

It's the output of seed heads of numerous grass varieties; clovers, dandelions, buttercups, dock, sorrel, ragwort (bohalawn).

The 'cleanest-winded' horse coming out of a sterile stable for exercise will 'clear his throat' once or twice! Author has no experience of more acute cases.

e. Grass-Land Herbs

Note: Dear Mr./Mss "Rigorously Efficient Manager" from all animals.

"You may get rid of the dock, the buttercup and the ragwort but please leave us the dandelion (good for our kidneys), yarrow for arthritis and sorrel; you'll know it, kind of 'refined' dock, antidote for hay fever.

The cows are 'mad' about ivy and all of us like the tasty new shoots of the briar-'spose it's their deep roots pick up all good things in the ground.

And as a special treat for a confined horse, Tom na gCapaillín cuts a great square of green sod; grass/clay and all; better than a tonic.

Another 'tip' he got from a friend of his in Sligo.

Cut a fresh rod of furze; down there they call it whin; and hang it up in the stable. Chewing it you'll never get bored or develop bad habits!

f. Grass Warts

Note: 'Proper' warts generally indicate viral infection.

The muzzles of pale pigmented, white faced horses; more particularly young, perhaps yearlings, at grass in summer will sometimes have clusters of tiny warts.

Dew covering on the grass worsens if not contributing to the condition; skin cracks and makes it more annoying.

Recommended taking afflicted animal off grass overnight, with a few 'pals,' for a few days.

Avail of opportunity for 'teach-in,' dressing mane/hooves, introduce to bit and bridle; lead in 'hand'; accustom to loading on box.

Release to grass after sun has burned off dew.

1. Note: Experts hold that species of parasites use 'dew' to climb up grass shoots; laying eggs; may be snapped up by horse.

2. Note: 'Smart' breeders will have their foals from 4-5 weeks and upwards eating say half a full cupful of foal pellets/day to augment mother's milk (which may be deficient in some minerals), ensures foal is 'self-sufficient' at weaning time.

3. Note: Cases of copper deficiency can occur; indicated by lack of 'thrive'; corrected by copper injection.

The trace element molybdenum in limestone ground interferes with the utilization of copper by the horse's metabolism.

4. Note: Calcium is very important for bone development, a pregnant mare, of 500kg weight must get 50gr. Calcium/day.

g. Blistering

Is applying a 'counter irritant' usually to horse's leg.

Has effect of stimulating blood flow to area, thereby promoting healing.

First clip hair from site - **<u>Do not</u>** apply to open wound or broken skin.

The process causes pain to horse; will be necessary to prevent 'him' worrying the location; fit 'cradle' restricting head movement and monitor behaviour.

'Practice' had been brought to fine art in times past but has fallen into decline latterly.

The irritating agent could be mercuric dioxide or similar and such substances may now be 'withdrawn' on animal welfare grounds. In most cases it will take hair six weeks to regrow. Formerly applying a 'charge' i.e. 'blister' to hunters' legs before letting them 'off' to summer grass was common.

h. Mud Fever

May afflict some horses particularly in winter.

It is caused by infection entering through cracked skin on lower legs.

Those standing in muddy fields or being ridden through boggy, poached ground will be most at risk.

Legs of horses after exercise may be 'hosed down.'

Patting with dry cloth and taking into deep clean straw 'bed' will give good results.

Another well recommended practice with hunters is to wrap soft dry meadow hay round lower legs allowing natural drying; clay will then brush out!

Application of lanolin regularly is beneficial; 'cracked' skin allows ingress of infection; continuous wetting depletes oils in skin.

i. Dehydration

Means that loss of bodily fluid through sweating is not made up by intake of drinking water.

Simple Check: Pinch fold of skin along neck; how long does it take to 'recover'?

If suspected; or to prevent, ensure clean fresh water always available; have 'salt-lick' or salt/mineral block accessible to horse in stable.

If case is acute, veterinary attention is required.

Note: ref. Irish Field Dec'97' 'Learning the Lessons from the Atlanta Games', attention is directed to dehydration/re-hydration in conditions of high temperature and humidity.

It is noted that horses can and will drink larger quantities of water.

More beneficial if sodium is added; becomes an electrolyte; you can overdose on electrolytes however!

j. Horse in Poor Condition

"Has he been wormed? So that's not the problem."

"Right! Start him on a tonic-that'll put hair on his chest."

Not so! Often it appears the "tonic" over-powers "his" metabolism and passes through without benefit.

A natural "tonic" e.g. flax- seed jelly on nuts/grain- 'all in moderation' will work better.

Come month of May and 'Dr Green'; the real Ally Daly; a 'pick' of new grass.

To 'turn him inside out' in earnest, cut/pluck a double handful of sweet vernal grass; seed head on point of ripening; full of protein; balanced by clean fibre stalk with the 'tint' of green (chlorophyll) still in it (mix with his regular hay).

Keep it up through the growing season; as other grasses mature.

Note:

Flaxseed jelly/boiled linseed is a cold weather/winter 'delicacy'/tonic.

With any rise of temp., or if not fed 'fresh' it 'goes off'/turns 'sour' quickly and will cause stomach upsets.

k. Stabling need not be Five Star

Here's all he asks:

Good ventilation (without draughts) to disperse foul air.

(At rest lungs inhale/exhale approx eighty litres per minute.)

Adequate head-room, minimum eight feet:

(Horses seem ill at ease with rain pounding on metallic roof above their heads)

Solidly secure to give heat and noise insulation; in the wild, horses would shelter in caves or forests.

Anything else?

Well, shaded corner to enjoy bit of rest and 'bay-window'; half-door, to give view of world passing by.

Bed - deep (6" min) and dry; 'banked' up in corners and along walls;

minimizes risk of horse getting 'cast'; lies too close to wall; difficulty getting to his feet; panics, threshes about; risk of serious injury.

Note: Young horses are nervous of lying down in new/strange stables, deep bed gives confidence; develops habit of stretching out 'head on the pillow', most restful.

Bedding Material (old term stable litter.)

I. Straw, preferably wheaten; barley, irritating awns; oaten, tempting to eat;
II. Wood-shavings, dust extracted: 'look the part' and pleasant aroma.
III. Peat Moss, often damp, can be 'recycled', gardening/horticulture.

Note:

- Impetuous horse at risk on frosty yard; spread 'mucked out' litter or cinders or sand for safety.
- A horse will pass seven or eight heaps of droppings overnight; good indicator of state of health; 'bound-up'; constipated; trouble in store!
- Good practice to paint lower half of stable walls black; if horse becomes cast or rolls in colic; 'marks' are visible.
- Keep sharp 'look out' for projecting nails/screws/wood splinters/loose or trailing electric cables and attend immediately.
- Regular check of guttering/down-pipes on stables and drains/gullies in yard.
- Unfailing old cure for confirmed 'bedding eater' was diluted 'pig muck' sprinkled on straw.

Take care! Horse is usually 'outraged'; won't eat hay off floor; safer options now are wood-shavings; peat moss.

'The Cold Shiver'

Force of habit; cheery greeting, a 'sweep' around with the 'practised' eye,
Not a bother on him! The world is a happy place; 'on Raglan Road on an Autumn Day'....
Sooner or later it'll come-the 'cold shiver down your back'!

"That leg's 'up' like a bedpost".
Now it's "he did not wring his hands nor weep" ----

Note: The horse is noted for extreme and rapid inflammation, with pain and 'heat', in response to injury/infection.

Fast attention is Full Recovery!

Likely vet's response is anti-inflammatory drug into blood stream.

He/she will have formed idea of cause; questioned carer, previous 'history', anything out of ordinary?

As inflammation disperses tissue/limb resumes normal shape, heat also goes.

Note: Good practice.

1. 'Scour' feeding pot regularly with bread soda and warm water.
2. Guard against contamination of stored feed: mice droppings and scavenging sparrows; discourage any cats loitering about the hay.
3. The food value of rolled oats, flaked maize and similar is diminished by oxidation (exposure to air); close bins and sacks securely.

Horse fatigued almost to the limit.

'Leave him to his own devices'- he'll recover; No!

Initially limited amount of water and small appetizing feed.

Repeat after interval, restores body energy, less likely to 'break- out'/start sweating afresh.

Weather and injuries, if any, permitting get him out in paddock for 'twenty' minutes.

Revitalizes complete system; accelerates recovery.

'He' is a creature of movement.

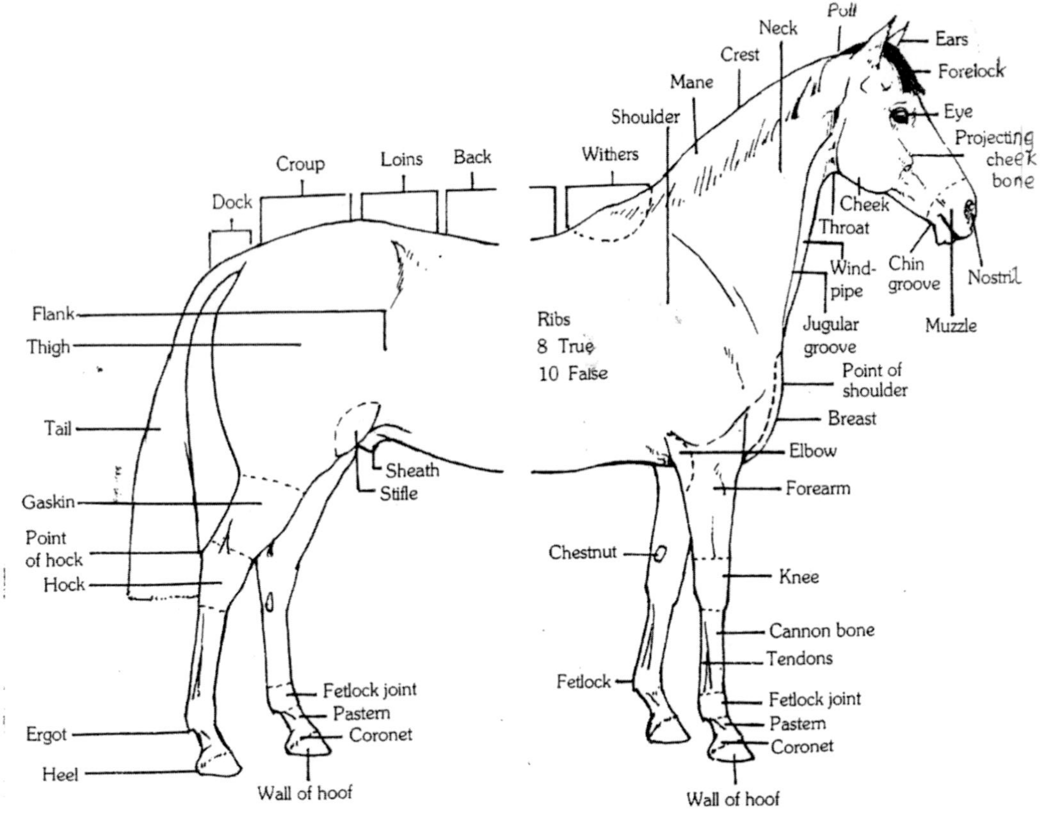
Poll
Neck
Ears
Crest
Forelock
Mane
Eye
Shoulder
Projecting cheek bone
Withers
Croup
Loins
Back
Dock
Cheek
Throat
Wind-pipe
Chin groove
Nostril
Muzzle
Jugular groove
Flank
Thigh
Ribs
8 True
10 False
Point of shoulder
Tail
Breast
Elbow
Sheath
Stifle
Forearm
Gaskin
Point of hock
Chestnut
Knee
Hock
Cannon bone
Tendons
Fetlock
Fetlock joint
Pastern
Coronet
Fetlock joint
Pastern
Coronet
Ergot
Heel
Wall of hoof
Wall of hoof

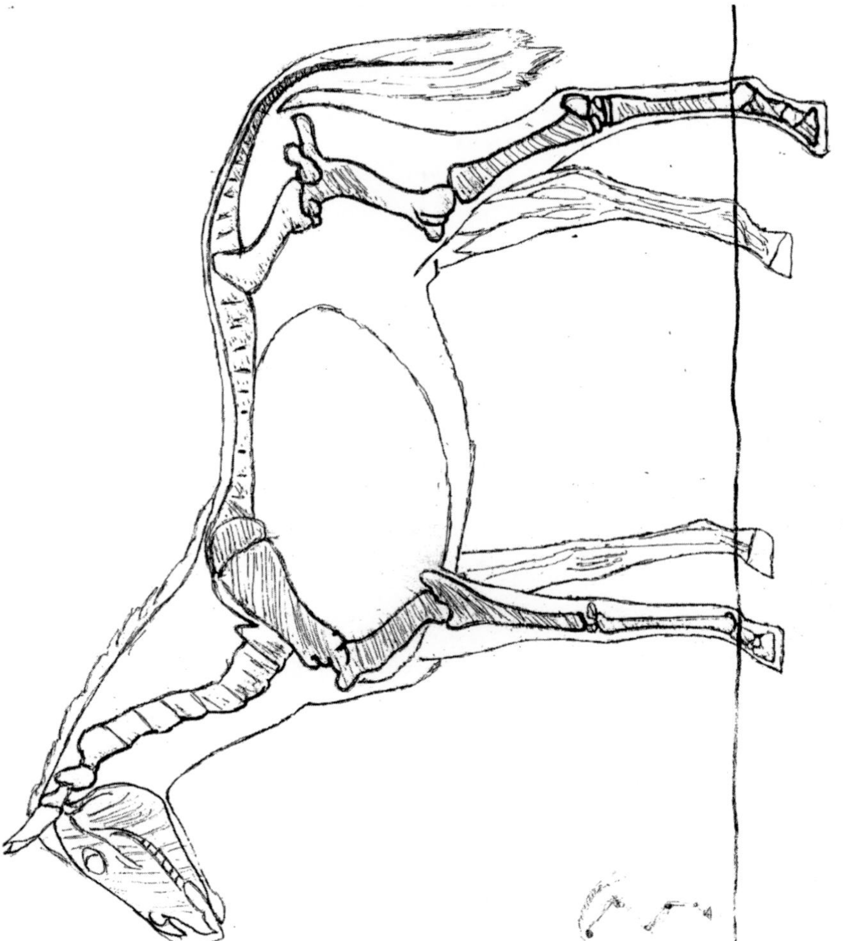

9. Matchstick Horse at Rest

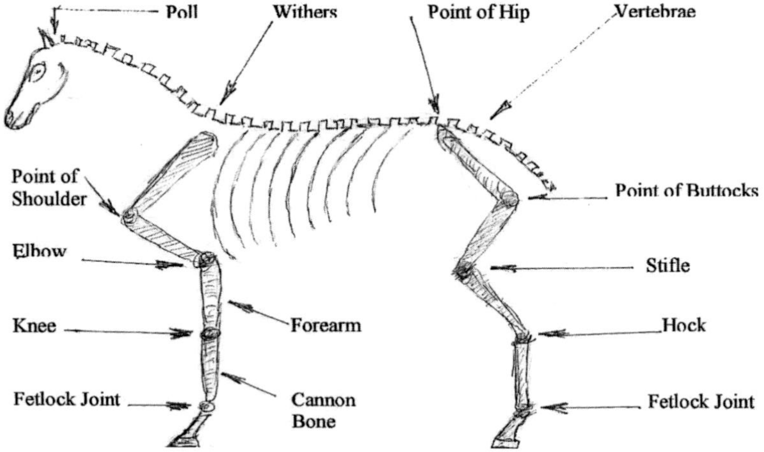

Note:

- The poll is a very sensitive point, subject to injury, horse throws up head entering doorway or while travelling in box!

Fit poll-guard to head collar.

- At the withers shoulder is connected to spine via pad of muscle.

A horse with 'good wither' 'carries' the saddle well. An ass has no wither. Height of horse measured from highest point of withers to ground; in 'hands' (4 inches) or metric. Example: 16h.2" or metric 1.68m is a good height for a 'man's horse.'

- Point of hip, could be injured going through narrow opening.
- Vertebrae extend from poll down into dock of tail.
- 'Experts' talk of 'good shoulder', 'good sloping shoulder,' not too 'straight in front,' your 'eye' will tell you!
- Good forearm (same experts) 'substance' in it! Not spindly.
- Good cannon bone (experts again) not excessively long, plenty of 'bone'; actually means measurement around cannon bone just under knee; 8 ½ to 9 inches for a riding horse.

Looking at any horse these 'experts' will 'squint' their eyes and see above 'matchstick horse' in every horse; fat or thin; hairy or sleek; but horse standing still is of little use!!!

- Has 'he' a good 'step' to him?

A straight swinging walk?

Does he 'track-up' (hind hoof approaches to/or extends forward of front hoof on same side) at a purposeful walk.

• Trotting: Do the 'piggies' come straight out at you or turn in/out or 'wind' a bit?

Uneven pressure comes on joints if gait is not straight/true and may dispose towards unsoundness.

Note:

1. Perfection is the work of the Gods (Ancient Greek belief!)
2. Trotting is not 'running' (see chapter 'making the horse')
3. The 'experts' will say above 'horse' is like a 'dropped' calf; 'all legs and no body'; they're right!
4. Matchstick horse is a very poor subject for 'toting' any load.
   Back muscles must be developed to take pressure off spine.
5. Good 'conformation' means 'all parts are in harmony.'
   Are legs 'adequate' to support mass of body or is 'he' top-heavy?

Photo 1: Yearling at Sales

Photo 2: Racehorse Galloping

Meeting the British: *Art MacMurchada Caomhánach confronts Richard II's representative, the Earl of Gloucester, in an illustration from the end of the 14th century*
Art Mc Murragh KAV.. 1357 – 1417

Photo 3: Art McMurrough-Kavanagh on his 14.2hh 'flying machine.'

Photo 4: Hugh de Lacy 'listening to the music'; first outing; Tara Hunt at Ballivor, owned, 'made' and ridden by Author. Bred by Mrs Patricia Farrell

10. Foaling: A Happy Event

Basically a simple procedure; going on all the time safely, given attention to hygiene and 'smartness' to recognize possible complications requiring professional intervention.

'In foal' mare, particularly in last 12 weeks (foetus growth 60-65%) requires extra food to ensure a strong foal and a good milk supply for that foal 'on the ground'.

Good forage, i.e. 'sound' hay; high protein nuts and supplement, calcium diphosphate or flax seed jelly.

Perhaps stabled at night or in sheltered paddock; 'pick' of grazing and space to exercise by walking.

'Bacon Pig' fat mare is not wanted; could have foaling difficulties.

Be attentive approaching 'Date Due'; look out for 'waxing up'; drops of wax on teats; foaling is imminent!

Have stable cleaned out; already disinfected with boiling water/Jeyes Fluid solution; and deep clean straw bed laid.

Let her use stable for couple of days; allows her immune system to 'imprint.'

Washing hind-quarters of mare before/after foaling reduces risk of bacteria 'take up' by new born foal 'searching' for udder.

'Night-watch'; be vigilant but don't disturb too much.

Have 'vet on call's' telephone number; listen for uneasiness, lying down, getting up; part of delivery process.

Foal can make appearance in a matter of minutes/seconds even.

If 'presentation' is normal, forelegs and head, don't anticipate problems. (If presentation otherwise, alert vet. without delay; he/she may give relaxing injection to halt process while manipulating position of foal).

Normally if mare's efforts are assisted tactfully, foal will 'slip out;'

With finger remove mucus from mouth, check breathing. With straw 'wisp', give a few vigorous rubs along back. If not already broken, cut umbilical cord and douse/spray thoroughly with iodine. Over first few days check it has dried up. Slightest sign of 'weeping' indicates infection requiring immediate attention.

Leave foal to mare to lick dry; 'bonding'!

Within short period foal should stand and suck; thus vital antibodies in the colostrum are ingested as soon as possible and evacuation of meconium from bowels is triggered.

If constipated lubricate anus with liquid of paraffin to relieve pressure.

Within 8 hours mare should have 'cleaned' i.e. expelled after- birth; check it's a healthy pink/no black/grey patches and all complete; it's like 'the map of France'!

Precaution: Women/Girls to wear surgical gloves.

Mare can be offered unchilled water to drink and warm bran mash or small standard feed.

Of course mare could foal outside in paddock in late spring; less risk of infection but makes sure other horses will not bother her.

Be aware of primitive instinct to 'hide' foal from predators; she may push newborn foal into briars or drain!

Now foal is running with mare; and sucking 70 times in the 24 hour. (Pity the poor orphan foal).

'Al Ham do Lla'; still keep an eye on them;

Note: There's 'your' foal four or five days old; out to enjoy a bit of sunshine; 'scampering' around 'mammy'.

Rest from your labours for a minute.

You have the 'match stick' horse in your mind.

It won't be necessary to 'squint'; everything's so clear, 'correct proportions; sloping shoulder; look how he moves'.

"Yes; he's a little smasher"!

Note:

1. Gestation period of mare about 11 month.
   Gestation period of ass about 12 months.
   Service season for mares February 14th - July 14th Northern Hemisphere.
2. Age of horse 'calibrated' from January 1 of year foaled.
3. For thoroughbred racing/sales industry, precocity is prized so 'earlier foaled the better'; though weather/climate is not so understanding.
4. It's now accepted that mare 'harbouring' a sub clinical infection will not foal according to the calendar; 'will carry a few extra days'; nature's way of ensuring the 'bambino' is strong enough before 'venturing out.'
5. Commercial studs are very vigilant of 'minor' scratches on mare.

6. Good policy to get mare and foal out for pick of grass and fresh air on second/third day weather permitting, gives opportunity to clean out/air stable.

   Do not keep mare and foal out for more than 15 - 20 mins for first couple of days (thinking of heat-loss to foal's small body).

   Foal is still virtually 'blind' so a helper is essential; aware of hazards; for safety's sake keep mare on lead rein.
7. Mare comes into 'heat' again after 9 days and hormones in her milk will most likely cause foal to scour; normally not very serious.
8. Remedy, 'milk her out' manually; a bit of privation won't do the foal any harm!
9. Transporting mare to stud is stressful for foal; stress makes more susceptible to infection.

   In a 3 hour journey, stop three times to allow foal to suck.
10. Thinking ahead, 'play school' and trauma of weaning; it is a good idea to have another mare & foal as companions.
11. Watching foals/yearlings at play is... enlightening!

    Who wins most of their 'chases'? and 'wrestling' matches (colts)!

    Not so nice! Who's 'the greedy gut'? Starting out to be a bully; has own share then tries to grab more!

    Bullying in older animals is infrequent but serious; kicking, biting, threatening. Timid animal driven 'in shock' 'out of herd.' Remedy, 'break up the gang.'
12. Where possible isolate in-foal mares from hunting horses or gymkhana ponies; there is risk of infection being carried in!

Weaning

A March foal should be well fit for weaning early September.

He's 'independent' now; knows what 'real' food is (eating half-scoop of foal pellets a day) and 'Mammy' is 'expecting' again.

On appointed day bring 'himself', a few of his 'pals' and perhaps a sensible older mare into the stable yard.

With minimum delay deliver 'the mammy' to distant location; 'out of sight/ out of sound':

In a few days there will be 'closure,' still keep apart; 'family reunions' are only for humans!

Note:

1. To stop a mare's milk flow; ('dry off') feed is reduced; definitely no lush grazing.
2. She can be 'milked out' for a few days if necessary (mastitis is a risk.)
3. During winter weanlings may be housed at night.
   Take in at 'sunset', good evening feed; nuts/grain with 'dressing' of flax-seed jelly and meadow hay.
   Adequate ventilation (but not draughty) is very important, otherwise sweating and resulting danger of chills is likely.
   Better to have individual stalls to prevent 'He got more than me.'
   Morning feed and out to paddock.

Thoroughbred Yearling Sales

Are a serious business and serious preparation takes eight to nine weeks.
The 'candidate'(s) is/are stabled at night.
After early morning feed the 'string' is led out to a selected path round nearby field.
Duration of walk builds up from about twenty minutes to one hour, balancing clockwise/anti-clockwise over the weeks; striving for a 'stretching' step and purposeful rate to develop muscles and put 'shape and make' on the juvenile form.
To prevent injuries/unsightly blemishes protective 'boots' are fitted and adequate length of regulation lead rein used (cotton lampwick webbing gives secure grip).

The yearlings are bitted, usually with straight bar 'showing' bit and use lead attachment so noseband plays part in control.

The handler, too, will stride out purposefully, 'aware of everything without looking' and regulating 'his' pace so he's shoulder to shoulder with his charge.
He'll wear protective gloves, knowing from experience how a provocative nip on the knuckles from razor-sharp teeth can 'go to the heart'.
'Take the pain'; some well-fed yearling colts are akin to fighting

cocks; spoiling for a row; may rear-up and use front hooves aggressively.

The order of 'the string' is rotated, each yearling taking turns to lead.

After this 'piece of work' the yearlings will be 'dressed over' lightly; hooves 'picked-out' and released to the freedom of the paddock to enjoy few hours sunshine being taken back in before dew-fall.

Amount and quality of feed is adjusted to reflect desired appearance at sales time;

'bloom' on the coat; reserves of energy to withstand a long day; balance between 'hard' condition and 'soft' fat.

On 'easy' days the yearlings will be coached to 'stand-up' on a level surface before 'the judge' for probing of leg soundness and height measurement, then 'walk away' and 'trot back'.

Even if they have previous experience of travelling by box it is well to give a few practice spins to forestall last minute stubbornness.

As most likely they will be stabled overnight at sales complex rations of their usual feed should be taken along, with tack, grooming gear and stable rug if worn.

Note:

1. Poll-guard fitted to head collar as precaution in travelling and entering strange-box.
2. In photo.1, see yearling 'pointing toe' well; displaying shoulder action; handler giving 'good' rein.
3. Mane well 'dressed' to enhance line of neck.
   Pulling mane (always underneath 'lie' of mane) may antagonise; 'pride is painful'; instead shorten by 'breaking' strands with fingers.
4. In 'walk-away and trot back' horse is always 'turned on himself' not dragged around handler; means he's collected'/balanced for 'trot-back.'
5. Driving in long-reins may be used with yearlings/'making' young horses to encourage forward-going disposition (requires competent handler and assistant).

Part Two: Follow Your Dream

11. Getting Started	42-46
12. Suppling Exercises	47-49
13. Gaits of the Horse Theory and Practice	50-55
14. More Mental Blocks	56-57
15. Another First-outing (Travelling by box)	58
16. Clipping	59-60
17. The Awkward Cuss	61-62
18. 'Prepping' a Horse for Racing	63-65
19. Marking Chart and Colours of Horses	69
20. A Bit of History	70-71
Index	73

Follow Your Dream

Keeping health and safety in mind; let's now follow our dream; teach 'Pegasus' all we know.

See 'the look of the eagle in his eye'; he'll 'dance like a wave of the sea.'

Get to know him, win his confidence, use all the senses.

The human voice is 'intelligence,' 'friend or foe'? to Ginger and Bruno and Hugo! They hear it like the 'grass growing'; identify with it.

'Stable routine' is a lot more than routine; it's dispelling fear; establishing trust; making a partnership.

Does bridle fit? 'dress' mane; pick out hooves; 'measure up' for a saddle and a 'hundred' other smartening 'distractions', while the atmosphere is 'all the time in the world.'

And in 'no time' he's ready for the next step;

no time? well 'generous' hour a day for a week.

Note: Keep talking and handling; 'distractions' are useful; they diffuse antagonisms.

- Won't 'play' with the bit; try a dab of treacle on it.
- Spirited young horse may develop 'contest' fixation with the 'keys' of traditional breaking - bit; may accept a simple snaffle quicker.
- Does he try to 'scratch' out the bit on some sharp corner?
- Or get tongue over bit (see it's high enough in his mouth)
- You, your presence, is important!

11. Getting Started

We're on' home ground'; confined yard; open space would be a temptation! Helmet, back-protector for the 'pilot';

Neck strap for Hugo, gives independent hand-hold; useful in an emergency!

And at Hugo's head the 'real Ally Daly' of an assistant; unflappable; a team player; rest assured he'll do the right thing!

Focus on plan; advance in easy stages from leaning across saddle to 'sneaking' astride with least drama while Ally pushes Hugo around in tight circles.

It's time for 'low profile', charming away fear, making effort effortlessly.

Ally, the 'main man' changes direction of circling 'keep a good thing going'.

'Don't give them too much time to think' as the old nags man would say; he saw all sorts!

It's time for a rest from this tyranny, slip off, going with the movement.

Ally will keep him moving; "brilliant Hugo; wasn't that easy."

Enthusiastic patting, re- appraise tack and repeat 'trick' before we grow cold.

Enough! we'll leave it at that; tomorrow is another day.

After lessons comes relaxation; a pick of grass; allows body and mind to recover.

Bit of grooming; vigorous 'wisping' along back muscles and neck restores circulation, then water and feed.

All in the day's work!

Tomorrow is Today

Too early yet for 'risk-taking'; just build on yesterday.

Start 'letting him know your there'; take up 'contact' on the bit; introduce slight leg pressure.

Any response? Still tense or 'freeing up'; you'll know through the saddle.

Active pats down the shoulders and along neck with vocal encouragement too.

You can see his character now; intelligent; willing to please; 'not turning a hair', confirms the opinion you had of him that first day.
"Ally, do you think we're ready to push the boat out a bit? Give us more rope"?
"We'll see; tomorrow."
"O.K. You're the boss"!

'Another Day ; Another Dollar'

There's a bit of adventure in the air.
Ally says 'fit a pair of subsidiary reins to the head-collar; you can handle double-reins"?
Means you have extra leverage for turning without pulling at his mouth and use 'opening' rein; moving inner hand towards inside of circle.
Leave nothing to chance.

Once we're moving he lets out a loop and we're 'on our own'; almost!
This is the time for 'pushing' through the saddle; asking Hugo to follow the bit.
If he trots a few steps go with him.
It's 'onward Christian soldiers' in earnest till Ally says "Kalas" (the Saracen word for 'enough').
Moves in; "Once more with feeling' in the other direction!"

Might not be as fluent this way; never mind as long as the effort is there; could be his 'stiff side,' will work on that later.
Thank God we've got away from the tight circles; it's becoming more 'civilized.'
I'm looking forward to tomorrow.

Take Nothing for Granted

"Bit fitting well? Not pinching the corners of your mouth? Hugo.
Your not one of those stupid horses forever trying to get his tongue over the bit"

Saddle sitting well, not rubbing the withers, sound!
A bit of repetition is good before progressing. Ally leads us round, demands 'more commitment,' stresses 'value of work' to us while he becomes detached; if still vigilant.

"Try a few 'figures of eight' like they do in the R.D.S."!
'Keep at it while I tack up the old grey mare, alright?'
'Stepping' around these confined spaces is O.K. but you've got to go out into the big world some time.
"Follow me" says he opening the gate and we take turn round the top half of the field, 'shoulder to shoulder,' mind on our job, 'no heroics' and back in without stopping.
We took nothing for granted, nor provoked confrontation; reposed trust in his good nature; yes, there is a degree of 'conquering your fear.'
Lets continue that way; there's 'tons of work' still to be done!

The Great Outdoors

You've guessed the next step; tacking up; getting organized; the preliminaries; 'warming up'; a few turns around the yard.
Then it's out with 'Uncle' Ally and the old grey mare round the field.
Down by Clancy's, round by Lake Victoria, up past the damson tree to the Sheep Gate; we'll vary the route on successive days,
Very pleasant but there's a serious side; the 'graft' never varies!
"Pay attention Hugo; that sloppy walk isn't acceptable;" 'collect' him; lift with hands'; 'push up to the bit' with legs; 'half-halt' the experts call it.
And the other 'marks' of the 'well bred horse':
Forward; Calm; Straight.

Forward means 'no backing off:' it's the unwritten rule, no ifs; buts or maybes!
The 'company' of a settled companion helps starting off.
'Growing up' means he'll 'face the music' on his own,
He's confirmed in it by the 'reasonable' will of the rider.
Punishment has no place nor 'Coaxiorum;' it's 'the thing' to do!
Bursts of exuberance go with youth and well-being; a good sign;
If excessive defuse tactfully; a harsh reprimand is out of character;

No jab in the mouth or crack of the stick; instead 'turn the blind eye'.

Note: Not a bit too early to start carrying a stick: think of it as a 'dressy accessory'; not to be used in temper.

The Loneliness of the Long-Distance Runner

Have you noticed the old grey mare is losing touch she has done her job well; happy retirement!

There's a world of work ahead for us; lets tackle it our way.

Rigorously scheduled plans only inhibit 'free spirits'!

The goal is responsiveness to the rider at all paces.

So he'll know to moderate his enthusiasm or be more energetic according to the riders 'signals.'

The rider will use tact and subtlety to convey his wishes and be tolerant of any hesitancy or misunderstanding

. "Give examples"! Certainly!

1. Going away from 'home' ask for a trot i.e. "squeeze/collect" to generate impulsion then open hands to release.
   He'll break into trot, most likely too fast; don't 'rein back' that's contradictory!
   Instead 'switch-off' till he slows down, patience!
   Then 'squeeze' him back up to desired rate.
   You're 'there' when applied pressure through saddle will maintain a working trot and removal of pressure is recognized as signal 'back to business like' walk.
   Don't think of asking for canter till this message is confirmed.

2. 'Heading for home' ask him to 'stride out,' an extended walk, 'offer' him the bit, he'll follow it willingly; common sense!
   Neat transitions e.g. walk up to trot, trot back to walk, improve the athleticism of a horse.

Note 1: The Highly Strung Horse

Is always 'on his toes'; persistent 'jogger;' very wearing on 'him!'

High energy feeding perhaps but 'problem' may be more deep seated.

To calm him, try this 'trick.'

Pretend 'asleep,' go with movement, minimum contact with mouth and rhythmic 'combing' of the reins.

Kind of hypnosis; 'Mind Game'; works in a week and is a permanent cure.

Leave 'straight' for the moment; you're working at it without thinking!

Note 2:

Here's how you'll know a relaxed horse; he 'wears' his head nicely (not star-gazing); back supple/rounded, (a good 'top line' the experts will say), movements fluid not jerky.

Any exercise done in this mode is 'pure gold'!

Note 3:

Let's look for improvement! "You're ready for a bit more commitment now, Hugo."

12. Suppling Exercises

A. Leg Yielding:

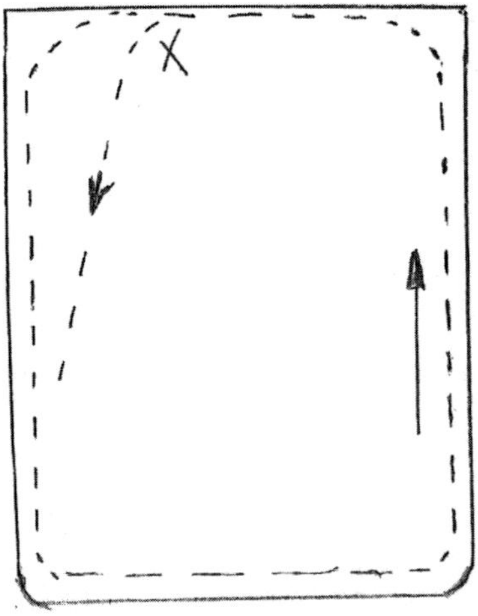

Is an easily taught suppling and strengthening exercise.

Horse has 'regular' path round field /arena.

Today 'by accident' he's taken a bit 'in field' at X.

Rider 'corrects error', still actively trotting 'forward'

by pushing with his/her 'inside' leg against girth.

Horse cooperates; his 'inside' legs cross-over

in front of 'outside' legs, until he gets on 'regular' path.

This exercise is 'asked for' at the trot- the horse is 'light' during floating phase.

With practice it becomes a great suppling exercise for shoulders and loins.

If direction of travel is reversed the 'trick' is still applicable.

This is hard work for a 'green' horse; do not overdo.

For Good Measure

What if it was a wet, windy morning: stay indoors? No!

'Business as usual' except 'rough' plait his mane when tacking-up!

Horses are 'uncomfortable' with rain in their ears; will lower head; 'work against the collar;' the exercise is more productive.

Back in stable 'thatch' horse; clean dry straw under rug; air circulating; facilities drying and no 'butt' of wet mane along his neck.

Towel dry around throat and ears.

Note:

• Even 'rough' plaiting will improve the roughest mane; soon it will be really smooth.

B. Lungeing

This exercise is to 'improve' the horse; establish a balanced trot, with relaxed curve through his body and rippling muscles along his back and loins.

It's not a 'letting off steam'; 'tug of war' with cracking of whip and ending in a 'lather'.

Find a reasonably confined area (25mx30m would do) with safe surface.

Horse may be 'tacked up'; given good head freedom. Accurate fitting cavesson over bridle and 'enough' (12m) lunge line for Ringmaster (R.M.).

Extra: Protective boots for Hugo and 'work' gloves for you.

The 'beauty of lungeing is sense of freedom; horse has no 'steadier' on his back; still sense of freedom can be 'embarrassing.'

Example: unruly horse decides "more fun to 'plunge' from A to B then B to C." R.M. alert to the 'game' shifts his base; keeps one step ahead "no short cuts auld son stick to the circle!"

Sending 'little waves' out on the line catches Hugo's attention; relieves boredom.

Should I try him on other hand?

No! Might only baffle him; provoke a 'scene'.

Do it first thing tomorrow; that way he's brought along till he'll go either 'hand' on request.

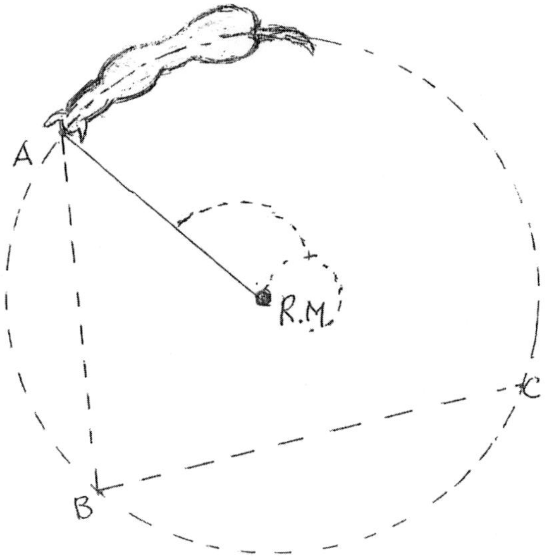

Note: Lungeing a 'fresh' horse (missed his previous day's exercise) is a sensible 'step' before riding.

Allows horse to 'free-up'; dissipate excess energy;

might also detect some quirk/lameness; useful with strange/new horse.

Precaution: 'Run-up', stirrups securely to prevent flapping about; use breast-girth to prevent saddle slipping rather than over-tightening girths.

13. Gaits of the Horse

You can 'see' the next day's programme.
Feed at dawn; tack-up and out to greet the sunrise; see nature coming to life.
Hugo's maturing in strength and attitude; alert for new experience.
So 'refresh' the fundamentals; like morning prayers!
Then think of something more 'technical.'

A. The Walk

A four beat; 'settling', 'stretching', 'working' gait.
There's a steady rhythm to it.
'Educated' rider can feel through the saddle as shoulder 'swings' for step forward.

That's the time to nudge it a bit more with the thigh; even 'push' the bit forward to ask for 'more.'
Rider will feel the hind leg come up under him also.
To 'make' a horse the rider must 'work,'
And the horse becomes audibly lighter on his feet.
(The walk is not the gait for fancy foot-work; always in contact with the ground.)

B. The Trot

Is a two-beat gait;
Off-fore; near-hind 'linked'as one movement.
Near-fore; off-hind in unison next movement, with a period of suspension, all feet off the ground, between the strokes.
For the uncoordinated horse 'his' trot will look like 'a leg at each corner;' tends to run: no sense to it!
To get it right let him ease down to just

above a walk.

(You know how to calm a horse.)

Then make effort, with legs and through the saddle, to lift him into 'timing.'

Even a few steps to your liking; be satisfied, let him relax back to a walk.

('An ounce of prevention is worth a pound of cure')

You can 'build' on that; so he'll listen to you; come 'alive', be more active when you squeeze with the legs/push through the saddle and relax as intensity of 'signal' is reduced.

Confirm him well in it now; it will be with him for the rest of his career.

There are various grades of trot, working; collected; extended; all will come naturally to him; he knows the fundamentals.

To have influence/control of your horse you sit in the saddle; means absorbing all the 'jolting' through the 'small' of your back.

You're not a bit rigid; you are supple; your hands have harmonious contact with his mouth.

To ease horse's back try occasional rising trot.

That means 'going with' thrust from hindquarters on one diagonal.

Lower leg remains in contact with horse, relax at knee, upward movement of trunk.

Come back into saddle and sit through next diagonal.

This is the time to 'see' he gets equal work on both diagonals.

When he progresses to 'figures of eight' we'll 'do as the experts do;' sit on the 'inside' diagonal, i.e. sit in saddle as inner hind leg comes under horse's body; taking shorter step; making it work a bit harder supporting weight of rider.

Note:

1. Look out for any tendencies to 'cut corners'; 'lean in on bends'; it's the 'lazy man's' way, saves curving your spine, they all get cute to it!

   Take control; half-halts; make sure he's square and don't overdo the 'figures of eight;' 'they're not everything.'
2. Remember what the 'expert' said 'good sloping shoulder.'

   At the trot ; extended trot; you'll see him reach out for the ground effortlessly, he'll glide.

   Don't get 'carried away'; extended trot can tax joints of a young horse.

C. The Canter

The Canter (slow gallop) is a three beat sequence.
i) Near hind 'kicks off'
ii) Off hind, near fore come into action, as a pair.
iii) Off fore takes over to propel horse into 'suspension,' 'floating', veering to the right.

i) At riders discretion sequence could be; off hind 'striking' off.
ii) Near hind and off fore as pair, taking over.
iii) 'Pole-vaulting' on near fore tends to 'steer' horse to left, good idea if track is veering/bending to left.

Note: It is an easy rhythm to sit to; relaxing for the horse also; he can fill his lungs during suspension phase.
A horse with a good stride can 'cover' ground.

The Canter in Practice

Usual progression is from trot.
If it happens spontaneously go with it; unbalanced; rolling like a boat as it may be.
Enclose with legs; ease weight out of saddle; 'give' rein; 'support' horse in your hands.

It's exhilarating while it lasts.
A young horse; a fatigued horse coming back from canter/gallop to trot/walk may become unbalanced.
Keep the 'leg on them'; hold them together lest they suffer injury.
(A fully 'accomplished' horse can strike off to a canter from a walk or even standstill and return to an 'ongoing' walk having 'skipped' the trot)
Spontaneous 'happenings' are O.K. for amateurs;
'on demand' demands a,b,c.

Canter on Demand

a. If at a trot collect, squeeze (generate 'impulsion'), lift into hands; the well practiced half- halt!
b. For straight line canter he can adopt either 'lead' (watch if he's favouring one more than the other; balance that out)
   Riders left leg pushes on girth to engage horse's left haunch, as the 'experts' say.
   Right leg behind girth prevents right quarters swinging out.
c. Release impulsion (open hands) horse 'should' kick off on left hind and go into canter sequence.
   If unsuccessful try again and again.
   If there is danger of spoiling a good relationship desist.
   Tomorrow we'll succeed with subtlety and tact!

Note: Happens a horse will perform some exercise with aplomb on day x.
On day x +1 "never heard of it"; "completely impossible"
Resist temptation to 'get thick';
Explain life is much too short to 'fall out' over trivial details:
You'll find it'll be 'old hat'! to him on day (X + 2), why?
<u>There'll be days like this</u>!

Note: Striking off with Subtlety and Tact

Scene-Appropriate Paddock/Arena

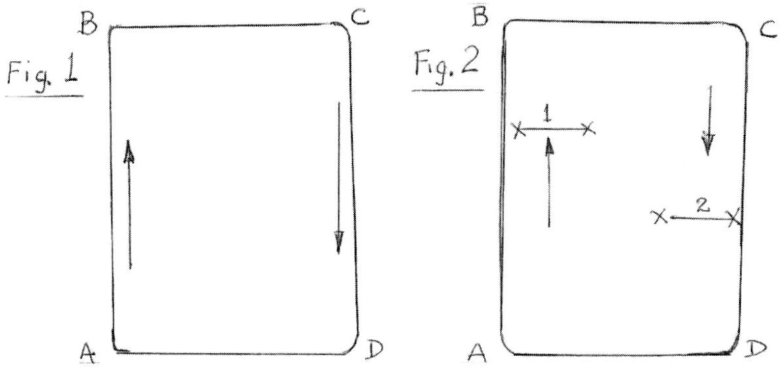

Fig 1: Trotting along side AB, approaching corner B ask for 'off fore lead'.

'Smart' horse can see two corners coming up quickly; rider gives correct 'signals', most likely it'll work.

Hold that canter through B, through C; back to trot early in CD.

'Ask' for correct lead coming into D; big surprise if he gets it wrong.

If relations are harmonious you may reverse direction and establish 'new' correct lead strike off; if not it will come tomorrow!

Note: A Mental Block

A 'mental block' has arisen; befuddling his brain, go to Fig. 2!

Railway Sleeper at X-------1--------X skipping over, all legs off the ground, 'he' will 'arrange' appropriate for canter stride on correct lead.

Back to trot after C, prepare for X--------2-------X-repeat a few times to 'fix' in his mind.

End for now; Hugo strikes off like clockwork on correct lead.

Note:

1). A well schooled horse and skilful rider can execute a 'flying-change' of leads while cantering. (The five day old foal in the

paddock can do it effortlessly!)
2). In 'counter-canter' a horse is purposefully cantered on incorrect lead (an exercise in dressage tests mainly.)

D. The Gallop (*Irish, Cos in Áirde*)

The gallop is an 'all-out' gait of four beats; the pairing of diagonals is 'lost'

There is still suspension, 'flying through the air'.

For grade 1 thoroughbred racehorses galloping stride of seven metres is attainable.

For show jumpers where precision/accuracy is essential the stride will be shorter.

At gallop rider will 'stand' in stirrups; 'out of saddle'; leaning forward to maintain balance while 'enclosing' horse securely with his/her legs;

Should not shorten reins/take 'tighter hold' as horse will 'read' this as signal to go faster.

It is bad policy to gallop a young, 'unmade'/partially 'made' horse; 'his' mind/body cannot cope with the 'frenzy'; risks undoing the good work.

Note:

1. Photo. 2 shows racehorse galloping yet not 'flat-out'; diagonal pair still 'united;' a characteristic of canter!
2. 'Length(s)' term used by race commentators is length of horse's trunk; chest to rump, equals seven to eight feet
3. Fastest recorded speed of racehorse on 'turf' is 42m.p.h.
4. 'Cute' racehorses while galloping can 'change legs' at their own choosing. Indicates discomfort/problem with front legs 'feeling' the hard ground. Don't ignore!

14. More Mental Blocks.

A. Horse is set a task; resists; doesn't understand? physically incapable? lacks courage? just wilful?
Rider/handler persists; horse becomes fraught; starts to 'steam.'
Stop!

Bring into yard, untack, hose down 'to the skin.'
Make respectable with sweat scraper; rinse out mouth with cold water. ('Old timers' would insert fresh bit).

Tack up again and return to arena to perform few simple exercises; not the problem one!
Invariably 'peace and tranquillity' will be restored.
Next day; trauma forgotten he'll perform the task 'unfazed.'
Has he 'thought it out' overnight? Latent learning?

B. Young horse refuses to enter indoor/outdoor arena or similar, Apprehensive?
Can quickly develops into wilfulness.
Resist invitation to 'bashing match'!
Find quiet, more mature horse and tether in arena, hay-net for company
'Herd instinct' will 'win'! The 'actor' will accept arenas for 'evermore'!

C. Imagine young horse/yearling, first 'outing'! Sales/show/strange stabling.

All novelty, new sights, sounds, people, other horses, would 'move a horse of stone': Becomes unmanageable, sweating: off feed,: tranquilizer? sedative syringe?
Try taking him/her for a good walk around the place, may work or could 'break-out' (sweat up again) on returning to 'box.'

Try 'Mind game'; bit of hypnosis?
Find 'empty' drinks can.
Imagine you're Damien Duff 'dribbling' towards goal; 'short tip' ahead; regain possession, keep going around 'pitch'/lungeing arena;

It exerts some fascination; is that shiny 'creature' alive?
Like magic the 'temperature' falls;`` 'fever' has passed, back to stable.
Don't discard silvery drinks can!
(The sedative syringe has its applications; has side-effects; be advised professionally before use).

15. Another First-Outing!

Nature never intended 'the drinker of the wind' to be transported by rail, road; sea or air.

He will have some instinctive knowledge/fear; but we have won his trust.

'Preliminaries'; accustom to trailer parked on way out to paddock; wheels blocked; no moving or tipping up; ramps rear and front lowered.

Lead through 'matter of factly', poll-guard fitted; accidental bump on head might spoil things.

Day of first outing, front ramp down, illusion of 'openness' but breast-bar in place.

'Positive thinking', confident walk up ramp, without 'breaking step' or backward glance.

Assistant to secure rear ramp/door while you tie-up, with slip knot and breakable string loop.

Remember old nags man's advice; "don't give them too much to think."

Get moving immediately; finding his balance will keep him occupied on short trip 'round the block.'

Smoothness; fixed course; anticipation; steadiness is the key,

And in no length you're back, unload to great celebration; a good introduction!

Note:

a. Unwise ever to exceed 40 mph-66 km/hr; risk of 'snaking'/swaying.

b. Horse likes to 'brace' themselves diagonally in box; give space!

c. Horse prefers to feel 'getting somewhere' rather than standing still.

d. On long journeys he is able to 'switch off;' can ignore noise.

Life is 'easy' for the 'good traveller;' doesn't expend nervous energy.

If horse ever panics; behaves badly, 'threshes about,' unload immediately.

There is a 'better way'!

It's much easier 'to talk to' a tired horse.

Cultivate connection 'trailer'-'going home-food-rest.'

16. Clipping

Starting late Sept./October/Nov. horses/ponies grow winter coat.
Begin to shed/'cast' late Feb/March to 'make way' for summer 'outfit'.
For horse in training/exercise/competing, a heavy coat will cause profuse sweating/dehydration with danger of chills and difficult to keep clean.
Remedy shed 'old' body warmer by clipping.
Let winter coat 'set'/finish growing; groom/brush well ; no tangles and lies well.
Now 'bring on' electric clipper going like 'busy bee'; horse takes notice!
Tell him 'it's nothing,'
Use show-jumpers trick; cotton wool in ears to diminish decibels in packed arenas; perhaps twitch on upper lip.
But above all persuasive voice and patience; patience; more patience.
It will work and is worth it.
He'll accept clipping for rest of his life.

Some impatient people use sedative syringe as matter of course.
Not fool proof; sudden noise can 'wake' horse with a start.

Clip horse in long even strokes against lie of hair, cleaning and oiling blades at regular intervals.
Ensure apparatus is well earthed; horse is standing in iron shoes on (perhaps) damp floor!
Most horses are sensitive about ears; take special care not to accidentally nick:
Clip face, under jaws and around throat.
'Style of clip' may depend on preference and likely use of horse.
See photo. 4, 'Modelling typical hunter clip.'

Even with most 'difficult' of horses/ponies do not use barbaric restraints; hobbling/throwing, extremely dangerous and mental effects remain for life!

Good idea after clipping to sponge horse with warm saline solution; cleans skin and attends to any minor nicks!

Fit with stable rug and perhaps warm under-blanket.

Horse will wear New Zealand rug for intervals in paddock.

Outlying horses even with full winter coat, will benefit from shelter as exposure to prolonged wind exacts severe toll.

Hedgerows, clump of trees often preferred by the horse to man-made field shelter!

Capt. Scott's 1911 Tera Nova Expedition to Antarctica used Russian ponies to pull sledges.

Wind breaks of ice blocks were constructed for the tethered ponies, who were fitted with tarpaulin sheets.

Was this, the first of New Zealand Rugs?

17. The Awkward Cuss

Sooner or later you'll hear……. Bravado.

"The 'bee' tried to carry me into the ditch; only for a cut of the whip on the jaw; I'd never have got him round"

It is Bravado!

What you'll do with 'The Bee'?

Definitely! He's edging towards the ditch/the stables; 'hanging' as they say in racing circles.

Pull on the reins with all your might?

No! 'The Bee' will only 'set' his jaw more; you're giving him something to fight against; you'll lose!

Take courage! Give him plenty of rein!

He'll follow the bit; head/neck forward and down.

Take a deep breath; two deep breaths; legs down around him.

Remember at canter/gallop he's 'in the air' part of the time, that's when you can turn him with your legs.

It's not the moment for triumphalism instead think "check his teeth" or "leg trouble"? Or 'bad thoughts' in his head?

Has 'The Bee' any other tricks?

He might 'take off'; a ruse to frighten you.

Alright! Two deep breaths;

"Go on you 'old bee', you're not going half fast enough."

You're not afraid of him.

If he persists, steer him into ever smaller circles.

On <u>no</u> account 'bail out'/ jump off (risk of serious injury, concussion, broken bones).

More Anti-Social Behaviour

Did someone say "that fellow might-rear up on you?"

"They did", faith, and he's setting himself for it now…

Act normal; if you're unduly apprehensive he'll know.

'Damage' limitation: no rough rider display; dangerous and problematic.

Stop riding; don't confirm him in his black guardism.

Instead 'harden your heart' and introduce to a tougher regime;

Let's see what 'he's made of' in the jumping lane (rider less).
Good drop fence; ditch/stream; double bank; 'things to open his eyes.'
Again and again; cruelty?
No! More like community service!
Repeat 'dose' daily and as the pharmacist advises 'make sure you complete the course.'
This horse will always require a modicum of firmness to keep him rideable; be advised by an experienced horse person.

The Rider and Anti-Social Behaviour

Here's how you'll know him.
Never stops 'picking at' his horse, clicking of tongue, flicking the stick, fussing with the reins, prodding with the heels.
He'll call it 'wakening him up'; it's not; it's confusing him.

Instead you 'sit quietly,' enclosing with the legs.
To 'focus' his attention grip a bit tighter and send a 'forward' impulse down the rein; a signal in the 'language' he knows best.

- At all well-regulated shows/events/sales there will be competent stewards/safety officers to guard against instances of ill-treatment/excessive punishment to horses/ponies; paying particular attention to practice arenas and loading areas.

Prepping a Horse for Races

A Bit of a Dream

There is a 'bit of a dream' in training a horse; it 'is' a dream with the racehorse.
He's only a 'baby' (not two full years), so don't overtax!
Still he has to learn his 'a, b, c,'! Forward; Calm; Straight.
Walk to trot and strike off for canter and be just as insistent.
"Pay attention"; no 'sloppy' walking; some day you'll be famous."
That's it; plenty of 'half-halts': bit of leg yielding; transitions; builds up muscle; makes him supple/responsive; so the jockey will say "you could put that horse anywhere in a race; takes a nice hold."

That's a long way off yet!
Has he got his 'anti - flu' vaccination as demanded by racing authorities?
That'll mean light exercise for a day or two.

Learn to go to company; bit of jostling; hold your place;
never mind "excuse me or beg your pardon" from those other cheeky brats!
In single file on the road to see the outside world.
Some day the 'class' will be taken out on the gallops led by a 'school master.'
It will be jogging for a start; 'warming-up;' dispelling tension.
Talk about 'through other' and bad language and one or two getting loose.
There's no 'short cut;' you have to 'get it out of the system.'

Amazingly 'the string' organizes themselves for a bit of a canter.
The 'lads' ease their weight out of the saddle; legs enclosing for guidance and a ragged hillbilly bunch swarm off.
"Least said soonest mended"!
With diligent practice will come order; learn to 'come back'/ 'collect' coming to tight corners; to 'stretch out'/ 'extend' in the straight; 'take hold' of the bit.
Stick to your own 'lane;' if others drift sideways move up, that's how races are won!

And the 'boss' will be looking/listening too.
How are the legs standing this?
'Any splints developing or sore shins'?
And 'his' condition; is he eating up? reduce feed if indicated or short break in work;
After 'work' walk on road to toughen up legs; 'lads' may lead in hand.
The 'day' can feel very long without some 'diversion;' so half an hour in the paddock of a sunny afternoon or a couple of miles hack along quiet back roads.

Like wine fermenting progress is made; don't rush, instead let it happen!
Some day you'll ask him to quicken; 'sit into' the saddle, take more of a 'hold', squeeze with the legs.
Not ready! He'll start 'digging a hole in the ground.'
Desist; 'all in good time' and after a few days; 'again', still not ready and then the 'magic' day!

You 'signal' and he seems to rise nine inches off the ground and 'goes on'!
If you're wise you collect him after four or five strides and smile to yourself.
And the way he did it, 'at the moment of asking;' he's got acceleration!
Now think about 'entering him up' (suitable race; suitable racecourse).
'He'still needs a series of fast 'spins' with a competent 'work' rider to make him more competitive and assess his preferred 'distance.'
Do not break his spirit, get 'to the bottom of him';
You want 'him' to be a 'Bill Cullen'; whose mother preached "You'll never meet a better man than yourself."

As the 'big day' approaches you'll have enquires;
"How's he going? Will he win?"
Just as well they don't know to ask.
"Does he give a squeal and a half a buck when you bring him out for exercise and did he try to eat you as well as his feed this morning"?

Note: Since you ask so nicely I'll answer your question "How long does it take?"

When 'he' was 'made' as a riding horse; knew the 'forward; calm; straight' business; walk; trot; strike off for canter; carry 'himself' well; no 'head in the air' stuff. (You'd want 'him' that way, whether or no).

Take that as the starting point;

Assuming no interruptions; injuries/illness, he'd be in good shape for his debut after twelve to fifteen weeks and there would be 'room' for improvement still.

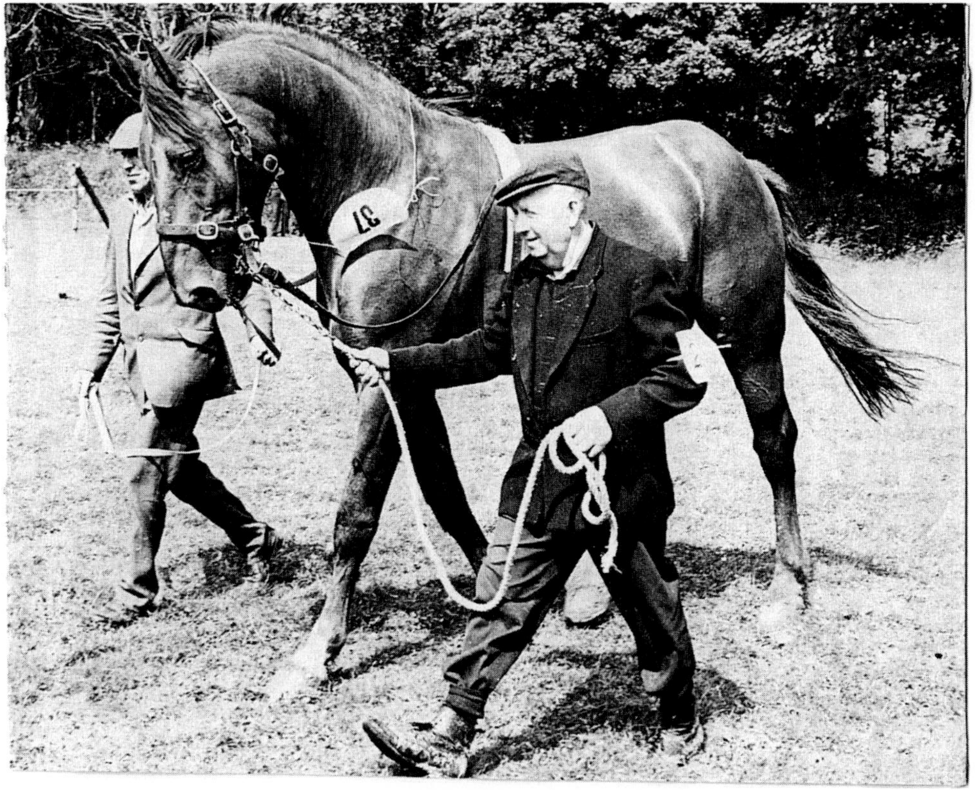

Dangan King, Irish Draught Stallion with owner Matt Doran Brosna, Co. Kerry; stood later at Kiltoohig Stud, Charleville, Co. Cork

NAMING FORM

(Effective under Rules of Racing Ireland and England and I.N.H.S. Rules)

REGISTRATION FEE

Under 2 years old: £[redacted]£9·2 and 3 years old: [redacted]£20
4 years old and upwards: £[redacted]£16
Half-bred for registration in IRELAND only £[redacted]£10
Fee for registration of name in IRELAND, already registered under the English Rules of Racing: £[redacted]£8

FEE DUE WHEN THIS FORM IS LODGED

No confirmation of Registration of name, other than publication in Racing Calendar will be given unless stamped addressed envelope is enclosed.

FOR OFFICE USE ONLY

TW	H	W	I	O
FEE				

COLOUR Chestnut SEX (Horse / Mare / Gelding) MARE — YEAR FOALED 1982 Name of Sire FLAIR PATH.

Name of Dam LENT LILLY. Sire of Dam EUDAEMON

FOR OFFICE USE ONLY

PROPOSED NAMES IN ORDER of PREFERENCE (IN BLOCK LETTERS)

Names appearing in the current edition of Registered Names of Horses will not be permitted.
N.B. Names must be limited to 18 digits including spaces.

USE BLOCK LETTERS

2 LULU LOVES MAGOA — 3. ~~FOXY~~
1 ~~FAIR PLAY.~~ 4. ~~SWEET Avondale~~ —

NAME OF BREEDER (if known) PETER FOX. COUNTRY OF FOALING IRELAND.

IF THE HORSE IS NOT IN THE GENERAL STUD BOOK OR THE REGISTER OF NON-THOROUGHBRED MARES THE FOLLOWING DETAILS MUST BE GIVEN

Name and Address of person from whom purchased or obtained ... PETER FOX, TULLYMEADOW, DRUMREE, Co. MEATH. Date of Purchase 6·1·1984.

If the horse was purchased at Public Auction, ~~the place~~ of sale must be stated, as well ~~as the name~~ and address of the previous ~~owner, or~~ person on whose behalf the horse ~~was sold~~.

Pedigree of Dam (if unknown, state so) ... S. EUDAEMON ex. LAST Count s. Final Score ex FRONDE

I hereby Certify that, after due enquiry from previous owners, the above particulars are all that I have been able to ascertain in order to establish the identity and antecedents of the horse, and I request that the name now claimed may be registered in accordance with the Rules as stated above.

Date 13.3. 1986 Signature T. J. Gillespie

Tel. No. 046-31613 Address 119 Boyne View, Avondale, Trim, Co. Meath

Name of Owner (in block letters) Please state title (Mr., ~~Mrs., or Miss~~) THOMAS JARLATH GILLESPIE

Turf Club Registry Office 18 MAR 1986 Curragh, Co

Account Number 26433

RETURN TO:
REGISTRY OFFICE: THE CURRAGH,
CO. KILDARE.

IF THE HORSE IS OWNED IN PARTNERSHIP THE NAMES OF ALL THE PARTNERS MUST BE STATED—THE SIGNATURE OF ONE WILL BE SUFFICIENT

PLEASE DO NOT FOLD

The certificate on the back must be completed by a Veterinary Surgeon.

Grindley-Dollard.

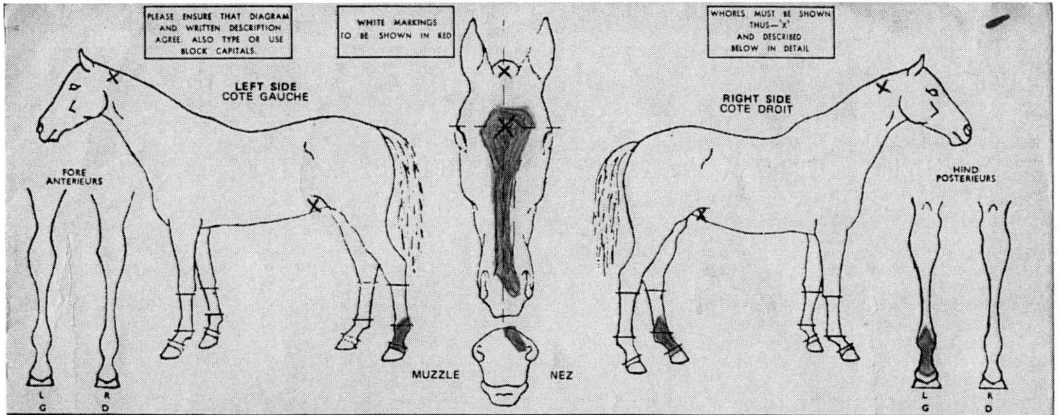

COLOUR *Robe*	SEX *Sexe*	YEAR OF BIRTH *Annee*	*SIRE *Pere*	*DAM *Mere*
Chestnut	FILLY	3/4/1982	FLAIR PATH	LENT LILLY

HEAD *Tete*: Median whorl at Upper Eye level Contained in a large well defined star with Conjoined broad Stripe extending full length of face to End between nostrils. Elongated flesh mark Contained at lower part of stripe Whorl at forelock.

LIMBS *Jambes*

- LF: No Markings
- RF: " "
- LH: White to ⅓ Cannon outer & posterior aspects, to ½ Cannon inner aspect & to above fetlock in front.
- RH: No MARKings

BODY *Corps*: Whorl past Poll left & right side, whorl on Right a little lower than left. Whorl in fold of Stifle left & Right side.

ACQUIRED *Marques Acquises*: None.

I hereby certify that the above diagrams and descriptions contain all distinguishable markings and physical characteristics

(*Names of Sire and Dam are based upon information supplied by the owner or his/her agent)

X

DATE OF EXAMINATION 16/1/1986

SIGNATURE of Veterinary Surgeon T.F. O'Byrne. MRCVS
(Not to be the owner or trainer of the horse for which the certificate is issued)

NAME AND ADDRESS (in block capitals) THOMAS F. O BYRNE. TRIM. CO. MEATH

TYPE OR USE BLOCK CAPITALS ONLY

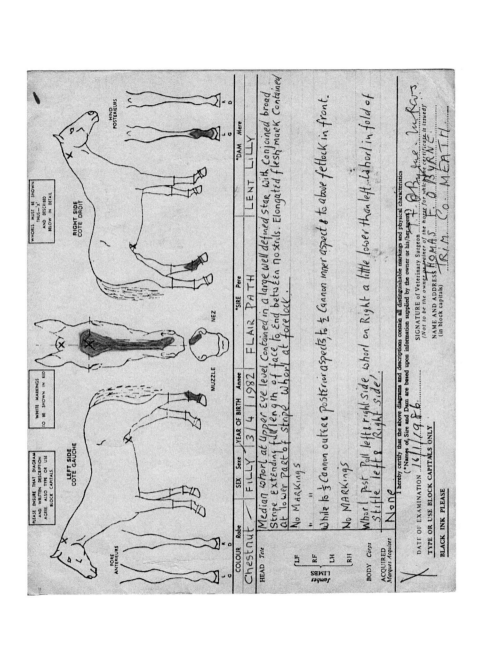

BLACK INK PLEASE

19. Marking Chart and Colours of Horses

Most traits of the horse including his colour arise from complex interaction of multiple genes (dominant; recessive; combinations).

Certain equine 'family trees' (Sire-line; Dam–line) may have an 'established' colour (either chestnut; bay; brown; grey) yet a 'random' one can appear.

Identification is made more exact by using blood-typing or DNA science

The bay coat ranges from pale coffee (light bay) to dark mahogany (dark bay). In early summer the light bay sometimes has an almost silver sand tinge.

The constant factor with bay is black 'points,' muzzle, mane, tail, lower legs.

If a hoof is 'clear' it may have dark flashes into it from above; 'ermine' markings.

Chestnut is reddish golden to old copper or darker (liver chestnut); the decisive factor will be clear skin/white muzzle: white (flaxen) or body colour mane/tail and 'points'.

Brown is darker than bay maybe almost black; can have white 'markings' on face; body; legs e.g. star; snip; blaze, flash, socks, as can bays and chestnuts.

The true black has no white hairs; in former times black horses were used in hearses hence prejudice against calling a horse 'black.'

Grey can be 'strong' colour when young; almost black /'steel' grey; chestnut/'strawberry roan' but becomes whiter with age.

Additional variations: dun, with (sometimes) brown/black stripe along spine from mane to tail, dorsal stripe.

Piebald (irregular black/white patches)

Skewbald (irregular chestnut, bay, brown patches on white), palomino, roans

Note: The coat and head/face may have a number of 'whorls'; changes in direction of hair growth (Irish-'ribe casta')

Location of the whorls marked on identity chart (see marking chart); another feature indicated by ▲ is the 'mark of the prophets thumb,' an indentation in neck muscle or else where; check it fits your thumb comfortably!

Note: It is said that taboo against trimming horse's mane and tail/ dock with scissors/knife came also from 'the Prophets' people.

20. A Bit of History

The Oldest Rule in the Book

It's 'action' carries weight.
Translate into modern 'speak', all the moving parts are harmonious; coordinated by rippling muscles, giving freedom and lightness of gait.
"He could walk on eggs; no flying divots from him as he goes up the gallop."
He can do the 'Maradona swerve,' depend on it he'll jump better and if he 'pecks' on landing he'll find a 'fifth' leg where others would 'flop' down in a heap.
It was 'in' him; it took 'work to bring it out'; half-halts; transitions; leg-yielding; you know the rest.

Note: Jessie Owens, Olympic medallist was coached "Glide over the track-it's on fire!
Same applies, to horse and human on 'squelchy going'.
'Brace the upper body muscles; lift', skim along the surface like a water beetle.
It's worth the effort.

Record Price for a horse in Ireland

In the late 14th Century the Earl of Gloucester and 'some' cavalry were making a 'courtesy' call in Art Mc Murragh-Kavanagh's territory; W. Wicklow/Carlow borders.
A.McM. K.-'flew' down from the hills to greet them on a 14h.2" pony-'the fastest thing on four legs' they'd ever seen; See Photo. 3
No Wonder! He had cost 400 kine; he was worth it.!
Note 1: Kine is archaic word for cow.
Note 2: Irish riders did not use stirrups-the Normans introduced them here-they'd picked up the idea while on the Crusades.

Prices of Horses-Abroad

Disputes about price of horses are nothing new, often going to court

.

Law courts yes and even to the Palace.

Remember the Darley Arabian; 15hh bay colt foaled 1700, in Aeniza near Aleppo, Syria and purchased by Capt Thomas Darley for three hundred gold Sovereigns.

There is 'talk' the owner Sheik Mirza II, tried to renege on the deal.

He even wrote to Queen Anne in London, claiming his horse was 'stolen.'

Anyway 'the headstrong one', the horse's 'pet' name, made it to England and became the 'Northern Dancer' of his day.

By the 1860's the 'going' prices (in gold) for desert horses were colts/stallions £200; Mares £300.

These were 'foundation stock' for pure-bred Arabian studs in England.

Note 1: The 'thoroughbred' had 'eclipsed' the Arab for speed by now.

The Stud Book was 'closed' to Arab horses.

Note 2: male horses were kept 'entire; Arab tradition.

Note 3: Mares were always esteemed above stallions.

a. Exert 'more than' 50% of influence on progeny;

b. Also 'mute' or more silent on 'raiding' missions;

stallion could not be relied on to 'stop his mouth'

Note 4: A horse could not survive under desert conditions without human attention (for food and water) so became almost a member of the family.

No wonder' the Prophet' spoke:

"To the just man a faithful wife and a fruitful mare."

[There are stories of dried locusts and figs/dates as feed and today bundles of 'green meat' (alfalfa) are sourced from nearest oasis for horses in cities]

Darley Arabian

painting by J.N.Sartorious

Gaelic Ruler setting out on a Journey on Horseback

INDEX

anti-social behaviour	61, 62
bone	7, 8, 9
'bone'	31
calming the highly strung horse	45, 57
colic	17, 18
emphysema	19
foaling/foals	35, 37
gaits of horse	50 - 55
grazing	15, 16
heart	21, 22
height	31
herbs	23, 24
ligaments	7
lungeing	48, 49
lungs	19, 20
mane	40, 47
'matchstick horse'	31
muscles	21, 22, 32
parasites	13 - 16
poultice	4
pulse	21, 22
ringworm	1, 2
safety	1, 2, 3, 42
sales	38, 39
shelter	26, 60
shoulder	31, 51
splints	8
stabling	26
stone bruise	4
teeth/wolf teeth	23
temperature	11
tendon	7, 8
tonic	26
worms/worming	13, 14, 15, 24